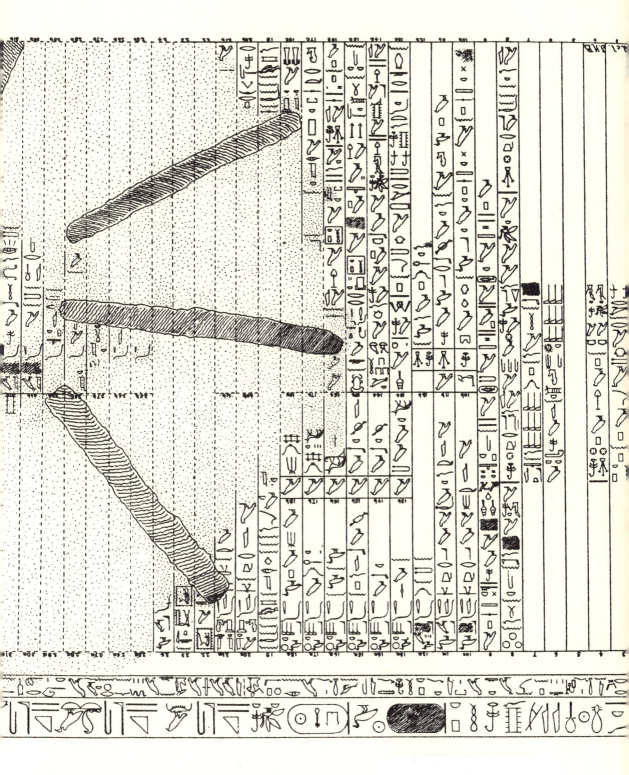

# Ancient Egyptian Science

## A Source Book
## by Marshall Clagett

Volume One

*Knowledge and Order*

Tome Two

# Document II.1: Introduction

## The *Pyramid Texts*

The earliest collection of religious documents in ancient Egypt is the so-called *Pyramid Texts*, found principally in the royal tombs at the end of the fifth dynasty and throughout the whole of the sixth dynasty.[1] These texts are written on the walls of the chambers of the pyramid of King Wenis in the fifth dynasty and those of the pyramids of Kings Teti, Pepi I, Merenre, and Pepi II in the sixth. In addition they are found in the pyramids of a number of queens of the late Old Kingdom and particularly in that of Queen Nit, the wife of Pepi II. We find them as well in the tombs of some nobles of the Middle Kingdom, the New Kingdom, and the Late Period, even as late as the thirtieth dynasty. In noting their long use, I speak of essentially unaltered texts and not of the funerary spells that developed out of the *Pyramid Texts*, those which we designate as *Coffin Texts* from the Middle Kingdom (see Doc. II.2 below) and those known as the *Book of the Dead* which originated primarily in the New Kingdom but also appeared in many later, altered versions (see Doc. II.3).

The texts consist of collections of individual statements or spells which are ordinarily called Utterances because they are introduced by the expression "Words to be Spoken". In all, the utterances number over 750, though the largest number in any single pyramid is about 712 in the tomb of Pepi II. They have no overall coherence and no single, all-embracing title. They reflect spells used in burial and offering rituals, and their oral character is everywhere evident. Traces of the ritual procedures of purification, offering food and clothing, censing, and anointing the king's body as well as royal and divine statues, can be found in the utterances.

The purpose of the *Pyramid Texts* was to ensure the resurrection of the king, his ascension to the sky as a divine star and as a companion of the sun-god in the latter's bark, and his enjoyment of the life of celestial regions with abundant provisions, regions where the king would mingle with and enjoy the company of the gods. The utterances also reflect the relatively recent doctrine of Osiris's resurrection and his role as king of the Netherworld (though this is not at all stressed as it was to be later).

We also find in these utterances allusions to the Horus- and Osiris-myths, as I have mentioned above in Chapter Two. The dead king had already begun to be identified with Osiris, the live king with Horus as Osiris's son. But despite these harbingers of an Osirian future for the deceased, the overwhelming emphasis of these utterances is on the celestial ascension of the king, an ascension that will result in his complete acceptance as a powerful god.

In selecting the extracts given here, I have limited myself largely to those utterances that bear on the cosmogonic and cosmological ideas discussed in Chapter Two. The most important thing to notice in this respect is that the king was identified with the creator god (sometimes as Re and sometimes as Atum) and his continuing governance of the world. Thus the utterances, though aimed at preserving the celestial future of the king, throw considerable light on the earliest expressed views of the creation of the cosmos and the nature of the gods and spirits that inhabit the Beyond. The identification of the king with the creator is particularly instructive in those utterances that describe the king as created in the Abyss before anything else (see particularly Sects. 1040, 1463, 1466). Among the things said to be not yet created are earth, sky, people, death, punishment, anger, turmoil, and in fact everything else that was later created. The role of magic in the king's ascension and power in the heavens is mentioned (Sects. 1318, 1324).

I stated earlier in my treatment of cosmogony that Heliopolitan doctrines predominated in the earliest documents but that there were also intermingled with these doctrines ideas that probably arose elsewhere than Heliopolis. I have mentioned in the notes the cases where Hermopolitan doctrines peek through the Heliopolitan utterances of the *Pyramid Texts*. This is evident, for example, in Sects. 265-66 and 446. The mention of the king as the Great Word in Sect. 1100 need not be a reference to the Memphite idea of the creative word (which, as we have said, no doubt developed later than the *Pyramid Texts*), since there is evidence for a limited doctrine of this kind of creation in the Heliopolitan system with its acceptance of Sia and Hu as creative conception and pronouncement.

The reader will notice that I have included a number of extracts that describe in a vague way the topography of the sky, including such places as the Field of Rushes, the Field of Offerings, the Field of Turquoise, the Mound of Horus, the Mound of Seth, the Jackal-Lake, the Lake of the Dat or Duat (usually translated Netherworld, as it later became, though at this time Dat had both celestial and subterrestrial components), the Winding Waterway, the Causeway of Happiness, and so on. Later documents were to fill out the details of life in these places in the Beyond, but occasionally we note some down-to-earth narrative detail that removes us from the mysterious or at least unknown references to ritual. Such is the case when King Pepi (Sects. 915-18) declares that he will be passed from mound to mound until he reaches the "tall sycamore tree in the east of the sky on which the gods sit", a naturalistic touch that pictures the gods as birds perching in a tree. The same kind of homely detail is evident when the gates of heaven are described as being of iron (Sect. 907), if indeed that is the correct translation since, apparently, only meteoritic iron was likely to have been known this early, and certainly not enough of that to conceive of great gates being made from it.

## Texts and Studies of the *Pyramid Texts*

The fundamental text is still that of K. Sethe, *Die altägyptischen Pyramidentexte*, 4 vols. (Leipzig, 1908-22). To these we must add his posthumously published *Übersetzung und Kommentar zu den altägyptischen Pyramidentexten*, 6 vols. (Hamburg, 1962), which is the most useful single work of translation and commentary that we possess, despite the fact that much has been added both in terms of new textual material by G. Jéquier, *Le monument funéraire de Pepi II* (Cairo, 1936- ) and *La pyramide d'Oudjebten; Les pyramides des reines Neit et Apouit; La pyramide d'Aba* (Cairo, 1928-35) and some significant improvement in the translation by R. O. Faulkner, *The Ancient Egyptian Pyramid Texts: Translated into English* (Oxford, 1969), with a *Supplement of Hieroglyphic Texts* (Oxford, 1969). Consult also A. Piankoff, *The Pyramid of Unas* (Princeton, 1968). For recent investigations and discoveries, see J. Leclant, "Recherches récentes sur les Textes des Pyramides et les pyramides à textes de Saqqarah," *Académie Royale de Belgiques: Bulletin de la Classe des Lettres et des Sciences Morales et Politiques*, 5e série, Tome LXXI (1985, 10-11), pp. 292-305.

## The English Translation

I have found the German translation by Sethe and the English translation by Faulkner the most useful of the various renderings of the *Pyramid Texts*. I have not, however, followed either of them slavishly. I have tended to use the titles of the utterances (or their parts) which Faulkner added to his translation, but occasionally have added my own where I wanted to emphasize the part of the utterance which I have translated. I have not adopted the first-person forms for the utterances, which Faulkner has almost everywhere employed. But instead I have kept to the third-person forms which include the king's name. I do this to maintain the historical sense of the documents, which disappears when the utterances are converted to model, first-person statements. Hence the reader will be able to tell from my translation whether the utterance appeared in the earliest corpus, that of Wenis, or whether it was first used by one of the later kings of the sixth dynasty. I have also abandoned Faulkner's translation of Dat as Netherworld since, as I explained earlier, the Dat in the Old Kingdom (written as it was with a star enclosed by a circle) included both celestial and subterrestrial regions.

I have included Sethe's section numbers within slant lines embedded in my text. The Spell or Utterance Numbers are distinct from the section numbers and are centered in my translation.

# Note to the Introduction of Document II.1

1. For an informative but brief summary of the *Pyramid Texts*, see H. Kees, "Toten-Literatur. 20. Pyramidentexte," *Handbuch der Orientalistik,* Abt. 1, Vol. 1, Part 2 (Leiden, 1970), pp. 52-60. See also the clear account of certain aspects of the *Pyramid Texts* given by J. Vandier, *La religion égyptienne* (Paris, 1949), *passim*, but particularly pp. 74-82. The specialized studies mentioned at the end of this introduction will give the reader more detailed information.

# Document II.1

## The *Pyramid Texts*

### Utterance 245
*The king ascends to the sky*

/250/ This Wenis has come to you, O Nut.[1] This Wenis has come to you, O Nut. He has committed his father to the earth.[2] He has left Horus behind him. His two wings have grown as those of a falcon, his two feathers (i.e. plumes) are those of a sacred falcon.[3] His soul *(b*ꜣ*)* has brought him. His magic *(ḥkꜣw)* has equipped him.

*The sky-goddess speaks*

/251/ Open up your place in the sky among the stars of the heaven, for you are the Lone Star[4]....

### Utterance 248
*The king becomes a star*

/262/ Wenis is a great one; Wenis has come forth from the thighs of the Ennead .... /263/ a star brilliant and far-traveling, who brings distant products to Re daily ....

### Utterance 249
*The king at the nose of Re*

/265/ ....Wenis has gone to the Island of Fire.[5] Wenis sets Maat *(m*ꜣ*ꜥt)* (the right or order of the cosmos) in the place of Isfet *(isft)* (the wrong or disorder of chaos) .... /266/ Wenis appears as Nefertem, as the lotus at the nose of Re; he will come forth from the horizon every day, and the gods will be cleansed (or purified) by seeing him.

## Utterance 262
### The king prays to the gods for recognition
/330/ .... Be not unaware of Wenis, O Har-Sopd. If you know him, he shall know you.[6] ....

## Utterance 263
### The king ferries across the sky to Re
/337/ The reed-boats[7] of the sky are launched for Re that he may cross on them to the horizon, ... for Harakhti that he may cross on them to Re, ... for Wenis that he may cross on them to the horizon, to Re .... /340/ .... The Fields of Rushes are filled [with water], and Wenis ferries across on the Winding Waterway. /341/ This Wenis is ferried over to the eastern side of the horizon. This Wenis is ferried over to the eastern side of the sky. His sister is the star Sothis,[8] his child is the dawn.

## Utterances 273-74
### The king hunts and eats all of the gods
.... /397/ The king is the Bull of the sky, who conquers (?) at will, who lives on the being of every god, who eats their entrails, even of those who come with their bodies full of magic from the Island of Fire ....

## Utterance 301
### An address to the primeval gods
/446/ You have your offering-bread, O Niu (Nun) and Nenet (Naunet), you two embracers (?)[9] of the gods, who embrace the gods in your shadow. You have offering-bread, O Amun and Amenet (Amaunet),[10] you two embracers (?) of the gods, who embrace the gods in

your shadow. /447/ You have your offering-bread, Atum and Ruti, who yourselves created your own bodies. O Shu and Tefenet, who made the gods, who fashioned the gods, who established the gods: /448/ tell your father[11] that Wenis has given your offering-loaves to you... [so that] you will not prevent Wenis from crossing to him at the horizon. /449/ For Wenis knows him and knows his name: 'Eternity' is his name, 'The Eternal One, Lord of the Years' is his name. The Armed Fighter Horus, who is over the gods of the Sky,[12] is he who vivifies Re every day ....

## Utterance 306
### An ascension text

.... /480/ It is Geb who speaks about it: 'The mounds of my mound (i.e. realm) are the Mounds of Horus and the Mounds of Seth,[13] and the Fields of Rushes worship you in your name of *Dw'w* as Sopd who dwells under his *ksbt*-trees....'

## Utterance 325
### A lustration text

/525/ The doors of the sky [are opened]. The doors of the watery firmament are thrown open for Horus of the Gods, on the first day. He comes forth into the Field of Rushes. He bathes in the Field of Rushes. /526-29/ [So is the case successively with Harakhti, Horus of the East, Horus of Sezmet, and King Teti][14] ....

## Utterance 407
### The king takes his place in the Beyond

/710/ Teti purifies himself. He assumes for himself his pure throne in the sky. Teti will endure and the good throne of Teti will endure. Teti will assume his pure seat which is at the bow of the Bark of Re. /711/ The godly sailors who row Re will row Teti; it is the godly sailors who convey Re round about the horizon who will convey Teti round about the horizon ....

*Some adrdesses to Nut*
Utterance 427

/777/ O Nut, spread yourself over your son Osiris Pepi that you may conceal him from Seth; protect him, O Nut ....

Utterance 428

/778/ O Nut, fall over your son Osiris Pepi; protect him, O Great Protectress, this great one who is among your children.

Utterance 429

/779/ Thus says Geb: 'O Nut, you have become spiritually mighty. Power *(shm)* was in you [when you were] in the womb of your mother Tefenet at the time you were not yet born, that you might protect Pepi with life and power, for he has not died.'

Utterance 432

/782/ O Great One (i.e. Nut), who came into being in the sky,... the entire land is yours; you have taken it, for you have enclosed the earth and all things within your arms. You have set this Pepi as an Imperishable Star who is in you (i.e. the sky).

Utterance 434

/784/ Be far from the earth, for to you belongs (?) the head of your father Shu.... /785/ You have taken to yourself every god who possesses his bark, that you may install (?) them in the starry sky, lest they depart from you as stars....

Utterance 469
*The king joins the solar bark*

/906/ This Pepi is pure. This Pepi takes his oar in hand. He occupies his seat, this Pepi sits in the bow of the ship of the Two Enneads. Pepi rows Re to the west.... /907/ The doors of *Bʾ-kʾ*, which is in the firmament, are opened to this Pepi, the doors of iron which are in the starry sky are thrown open for this Pepi, and he goes through them.... /909/ ...I am a star *(nḥḥ)*, companion of a star *(nḥḥ)*. This Pepi becomes a star.

## Utterance 470
### A collection of spells

/914/ 'O Bull of Offerings, bend down your horn and let this Pepi pass,' so says Pepi. 'Where are you going?' 'This Pepi is going to the sky, for all life and dominion, /915/ that he may see his father, that he may see Re.' 'To the High Mounds [or] to the Mounds of Seth?' /916/ 'The High Mounds will pass him on to the Mounds of Seth, to that tall sycamore tree in the east of the sky on which the gods sit'.... /918/ This Pepi has bathed in the Field of Rushes, this Pepi is clothed in the Field of Khoprer, and Pepi finds Re there....

## Utterance 472
### A ferryman text

/924/ The sky quivers, the earth quakes before this Pepi, for this Pepi is a magician *(ḥkʾw)*, Pepi possesses magic. /925/ This Pepi has come that he may glorify Orion and set Osiris at the head, and that he may set the gods upon their thrones. O *Mʾ-ḥʾf*, Bull of the gods, bring this (i.e. the ferry) to this Pepi and set him on that [yonder] side.

### Utterance 473
#### The king crosses the Celestial River

... /934/ This Pepi comes forth on this eastern side of the sky where the gods were born, and this Pepi was born as Horus, as Him of that horizon; /935/ this Pepi is acclaimed just (i.e. vindicated) and this Pepi's ka is acclaimed just. So, acclaim Pepi and this Pepi's ka, for Sothis (Sirius) is the sister of Pepi, and the Morning Star is Pepi's child.[15] /936/ This Pepi will come with you and wander with you in the Field of Rushes; he will serve as herdsman with you in the Field of Turquoise ....

### Utterance 477
#### Osiris and the king's services to him

.... /964/ ....This Pepi has come to you, O Osiris. This Pepi will wipe your face, he will clothe you with the clothing of a god.[16] He will do the purification ceremony for you at Djedit. /965/ It is Sothis (Sirius) your beloved daughter who prepares the yearly sustenance for you in this her name of 'Year'(Rnpt)....

### Utterance 486
#### Address to the primitive waters

/1039/ Hail to you, you waters which Shu has brought, which the two sources lifted up, the waters in which Geb bathed his limbs. Hearts were pervaded with fear, hearts were pervaded with terror /1040/ when this Pepi was born in the Abyss before the sky came into being, before the earth came into being, before any established thing came into being, before tumult came into being, before that fear which arose on account of the Eye of Horus came into being ....

## Utterance 504
### *The king's clear way to the sky*
.... /1086/ .... He (i.e. the king) takes for himself his throne which is in the Field of Rushes /1087/ and he descends to the southern region of the Field of Offerings.

## Utterance 506
### *The parts of the king are various entities*
.... /1100/ The lips of Pepi are the Two Enneads; Pepi is the Great Word....[17]

## Utterance 510
### *A miscellany of spells*
.... /1143/.... Pepi takes possession of the sky, its pillars, its stars. /1144/ The gods come to him bowing; the spirits follow (i.e. serve) Pepi because of his power *(bʒi)*. They have broken their staffs and smashed their weapons /1145/ because Pepi is a great one and the son of a great one, whom Nut bore .... /1146/ Pepi is the effluent fluid; he has come forth from the creating of the waters; he is a snake of many coils. This Pepi is the scribe of the god's book, who says what will be and what will not be created....

## Utterance 511
### *The king goes to the sky*
.... /1156/ .... he (the king) will hold up the sky with life and support the earth with joy; his right hand will support the sky with a *wʒs*-staff, and his left will support the earth with joy ....

## Utterance 512
### *Speeches by the dead king's son*

.... /1164/ Oho, raise yourself, Pepi, receive these four pleasant *nmst*-jars, wash yourself in the Jackal-Lake, be cleansed in the Lake of the Dat, be purified on top of your lotus-flower in the Field of Rushes. /1165/ Cross the sky, make your abode in the Field of Offerings among the gods who have gone to their kas. Sit upon your throne of iron, /1166/ receive your mace and scepter, that you may lead those in the Abyss *(nw)*, that you may give commands to the gods, and establish a spirit in his spirit-state. /1167/ Run your course, row your waterway like Re over the banks of the sky. O Pepi, raise yourself up and go into your spirit-state.

## Utterance 518
### A ferryman text
/1193/ O *Iw*, ferryman of the Field of Offerings, bring this [ferry] to this Pepi, for Pepi is the one who goes, Pepi is the one who goes.... /1196/ This Pepi has descended with the Two Enneads in the cool waters. Pepi is the potter (*or in other texts*, the plumbline[18]) of the Two Enneads by means of which the Field of Offerings was founded .... /1198/ .... The causeway north of the Field of Offerings is called the Causeway of Happiness. /1199/ Stand up, Osiris. Commend this Pepi to the supervisors of the Causeway of Happiness north of the Field of Offerings just as you commended Horus to Isis on that day you made her pregnant. /1200/ Let Pepi eat of the fields and drink of the pools within the Field of Offerings.

## Utterance 527
### The Creation of Shu and Tefenet
/1248/ Atum is he who came into being [alone], who masturbated in On (i.e. Heliopolis). He took his penis in

his hand that he might ejaculate thereby, and so were born the twins Shu and Tefenet....

## Utterance 537
### A resurrection text

/1298/ O Pepi, stand up and sit upon the throne of Osiris! Your whole flesh is that of Atum .... /1299/ ....Stand up. You shall not perish, you shall not be destroyed, /1300/ but live, O Pepi! Your mother Nut grasps hold of you that she may embrace you, and Geb takes your hand .... /1301/ May you go out as Horus of the Netherworld who is at the head of the Imperishable Stars, may you live as the living scarabaeus-beetle, as long-lasting as the _dd_-pillar, for ever and ever.

## Utterance 539
### An ascension text

/1303/ The head of this Pepi is a vulture. He will ascend and rise up to the sky. The sides of the head of this Pepi are the starry sky of the god. He will ascend and rise up to the sky .... /1304/ .... The face of this Pepi is Wepwawet .... /1305/ The eyes of this Pepi are the Great One at the head of the Souls of On....The nose of this Pepi is Thoth....[and so on through the body down to the toes, with each part related to a divinity and with the constant repetition of the ascension of Pepi] .... /1316/ Pepi is the companion of a god, the son of a god; .... /1318/ Pepi was born for Re; he will ascend and rise up to the sky. The magic belonging to him is that which is in the belly of Pepi .... /1324/ It is not Pepi who says this to you, you gods. It is Magic who says this to you, you gods....

## Utterance 570
### *Some miscellanies concerning the king*

.... /1453/ This Pepi escapes his day of death just as Seth escaped [his day of death] .... [And successively Pepi escapes his half-months of death, his months of death, his year of death as Seth had escaped his.]

### *The king becomes a star*

/1454/ Do not tread on (i.e. break up) the ground, O you Arms of Pepi which lift up the sky as Shu. [The bones of Pepi are iron] and his limbs are the Imperishable Stars. /1455/ Pepi is a star which illumines the sky. Pepi mounts up to the god that he may be protected. The sky will not be devoid of this Pepi and this earth will not be devoid of this Pepi forever. /1456/ This Pepi lives a life beside you, you gods of the Lower Sky, the Imperishable Stars [who traverse the Land of Libya, who lean on] their $\underline{d}^cm$-staffs. This Pepi leans with you on a $w^js$-staff and on a $\underline{d}^cm$-staff .... /1462/.... This one who belongs to the first generation for punishment(?) and for vindication, /1463/ which was born before anger came into being, which was born before noise came into being, which was born before strife came into being, which was born before tumult came into being....

## Utterance 571
### *The king is the son of Atum and is a star*

/1466/ The mother of Pepi was [pregnant] with him, he who was in the Lower Sky. This Pepi was fashioned by his father Atum before the sky came into being, before the earth came into being, before people came into being, before the gods were born, before death came into being. /1467/ This Pepi escapes [his] day of death just as Seth escaped his day of death .... /1468/ .... this

Pepi will not die on account of any death, /1469/ for Pepi is an Imperishable Star, son of the Great Sky-goddess who dwells in the Mansion of Selket ....

## Utterance 576
### A resurrection text
..../1508/ Pepi is conceived for Re, he is born for Re. Pepi is your seed, O Re, in this your name of Horus at the Head of the Spirits, star which crosses /1509/ the sea....

## Utterance 587
### An address to the sun-god
/1587/ Hail to you, Atum. Hail to you, [Khoprer] who created yourself. May you be high in your name of 'Height'. May you come into being in your name of Khoprer....

## Utterance 593
### Part of a resurrection text
.... /1636/ Your seed goes into her, she being ready as Sothis.[19] Har-Sopd has come forth from you in your name of Horus Who is in Sothis. You have spirit-state in him, in his name of Spirit Which is in the *Dndrw*-bark ....

## Utterance 600
### A prayer for the king and his pyramid
/1652/ O Atum-Khoprer, you became high on the Height. You rose up as the *bnbn*-stone in the Mansion of the Phoenix in On (i.e. Heliopolis). You spat out Shu, you expectorated Tefenet[20] /1653/ and set your arms about them like a ka-symbol, that your ka might be in them. O Atum, set your arms about Merenre, about this

construction, about this pyramid like a ka-symbol, that the ka of Merenre might be [in it, enduring forever] .... /1655/ O you Great Ennead, which dwells in On: Atum, Shu, Tefenet, Geb, Nut, Osiris, Isis, Seth, and Nephthys; O you children of Atum, extend his [good] wishes to his child in your name of the "Nine Extensions".[21]

## Utterance 660
### *The king is the son of Atum*
/1870/ O Shu, this Osiris Neferkare (i.e. Pepi II) is a son of Atum. You are the eldest son of Atum, his first-born. /1871/ Atum has spat you out from his mouth in your name of Shu....

## Utterance 697
### *A resurrection text*
.... /2172/ She bears you, O Neferkare, like Orion. She establishes your abode at the head of the Conclaves. Neferkare shall go aboard this bark like Re on the banks of the Winding Waterway. /2173/ Neferkare shall be rowed by the Unwearying Stars and shall give commands to the Imperishable Stars....

# Notes to Document II.1

1. Faulkner changes third-person forms here to first-person forms, as he does throughout, on the assumption that this was the original practice, though all of the texts we have give the third-person forms in most places. See also Sethe, *Übersetzung und Kommentar*, Vol. 1, p. 237.

2. That is, he has made the obligatory burial of his father. He goes on to note that his son Horus has succeeded him on earth.

3. The deceased king takes the form of a falcon so that he can fly up to the sky. In brief, he must have some physical means to get there. The falcon-wings give him that means and in addition stress his basic connection with the sacred falcon of Horus.

4. R. O. Faulkner, "The King and the Star-Religion in the Pyramid Texts," *JNES*, Vol. 25 (1966), pp. 160-61 (full article, pp. 153-61), suggests that the Lone Star is Venus seen just after sunset.

5. This spell reflects the Hermopolitan cosmogony of the sun's first appearance on the Island of Fire, which I mentioned in Chapter Two. The king here identifies himself with the lotus-blossom at Re's nose.

6. I have included this line simply because it is one of the many that establish a relationship between Horus and the star Sirius. Usually Har-Sopd is said to be the offspring of Osiris and Isis as the goddess Sothis. This line comes in the midst of similar addresses to the various gods asking them to take cognizance of the king so that he in turn will take cognizance of them.

7. Apparently the earliest form of the solar bark

was the simple reed-boat known on the Nile from the very earliest times. These boats are a far cry from the elaborate boats pictured in the *Book of Amduat*, and even more so from the boat discovered at the bottom of the south side of the Great Pyramid, which was presumably the solar boat that Cheops would sail across the sky (see N. Jenkins, *The Boat Beneath the Pyramid: King Cheops' Royal Ship* [New York, 1980]).

8.  Here the king's sister is identified as the star-goddess Sothis (Sirius).

9.  Sethe, *Übersetzung und Kommentar*, Vol. 2, p. 232, translates this as "Quellen (? Ursprünge)" because of the role played by the primordial creator gods. Faulkner rejects this translation because of the word's root-identity with the verb that follows, so that he translates the noun as "protectors(?)" and the verb as "protect". I prefer "embracers" and "embrace" in order to emphasize that the gods were born within and under the embrace of these primordial gods. See also the next note.

10.  We have here the mention of four of the traditional Ogdoad of Hermopolis: Nun, Naunet, Amun, and Amaunet. They are all described as "embracers" of the gods, while the gods Atum and Ruti, which follow, are described as self-creators. Then Shu and Tefenet are said to have fashioned the (succeeding) gods. Here then we have a mixture of Heliopolitan and Hermopolitan doctrines. Incidentally, Ruti is a dual personage embracing Shu and Tefenet, who are, however, individually mentioned immediately thereafter.

11.  Who the father is, is not clear.

12.  This is probably another reference to Horus and the stars; this time Horus is said to be "over the gods of the sky" (no doubt the stars), i.e. their ruler.

13.   It is made clear in other passages that, though Geb, the god of the earth, is said to be the ruler of these two Mounds of Horus and Seth, the mounds are in fact of celestial location. See particularly Sects. 915-16 below.

14.   Hence it is evident that the king Teti joins (and no doubt is at one with) four forms of Horus: Horus of the Gods, Harakhti (Horus of the Horizon), Horus of the East, and Horus of Sezmet. He meets and bathes with them in the Field of Rushes.

15.   The king is sometimes seen as the Morning Star itself (see Faulkner, "The King and the Star-Religion," p. 161). As Faulkner says, there is little doubt that the Morning Star is Venus as seen at dawn.

16.   Though in heaven, the king is performing the temple ritual that is performed on earth. Parts of that ritual are wiping the face of Osiris, clothing him in the proper dress for a god, and generally performing the purification ritual done at Djedit.

17.   This may reflect the doctrine of the creative word, which, as I have said in Chapter Two, apparently had early roots in the Heliopolitan doctrines.

18.   In Pepi's text, the king is called "potter", but in the texts of Merenre and Pepi II "plumbline" is found.

19.   Here Isis is identified as the goddess in Sothis (Sirius). Notice the play on words involved in the Egyptian name for "Sothis" and the Egyptian word for "ready" since both of them have the root letters *s, p, d.*

20.   A play on words is involved in the doctrine of the creation of Shu and Tefenet by spitting. Similar in sound to Shu is the word *išš*, which means "to spit out". Further, similar to the sound of Tefenet is the word *tf*, which also means "to spit".

21.   The expression "Nine Extensions" refers to

the basic idea that the Ennead represented the nine extensions of the form or being of Atum. Faulkner translates the expression rather as "Nine Bows", the traditional enemies of Egypt, which makes no sense here, though perhaps he thought it to represent some kind of play on words, since the verb "to extend" and the word for "bow" share the same hieroglyph.

# Document II.2: Introduction

## The *Coffin Texts*

From the end of the Old Kingdom through the establishment and the development of the Middle Kingdom a new form of funerary texts appeared, the so-called *Coffin Texts*. These were written on the sides, the lids, and the bottoms of the coffins of nobles. The coffins from which the modern edition of these texts has been edited come from all parts of Egypt, but the greatest number are from Middle Egypt, especially from the necropolises at Asyut, el-Bersha, Beni Hasan, and Meir, where great nobles exercised much of the power that the kings had held to themselves in the Old Kingdom. Also used were coffins from Lisht, Dashur, and Saqqara. In Upper Egypt a principal source was coffins from Thebes, with some coffins from Aswan, Gebelein, Dendera, and Abydos.[1]

The spells that comprise these texts were of a character not unlike those of the *Pyramid Texts*, which we have already examined in Document II.1. In fact, a significant number of coffins contain spells taken directly from the *Pyramid Texts*; these have not been included in de Buck's great edition of the *Coffin Texts* and will not be discussed here since we have already completed our examination of the *Pyramid Texts*. But the spells, whatever their origins, were composed on the behalf of nobles rather than for kings. This extension from royalty to nobility of the practice of including burial spells with the deceased to help him in the underworld has been rather extravagantly called the democratization of the hereafter, "extravagantly", I say, because the deceased represented in these coffins were not ordinary people but those grandees in obvious control of the nomes or regions of Egypt. For it is clear that with the collapse of the Old Kingdom a significant social change took place that was reflected in the *Coffin Texts*. In view of the exalted position in the Old Kingdom of the king, who was not only the living Horus but also called himself the Son of Re, it is not surprising that there should have developed a special view of resurrection in the hereafter in which the king retained the life and privileges which he enjoyed on earth. But as political power slipped from the king's hand and the nobles absorbed the effective power, they also absorbed the royal benefits, one of which was an elaborate burial accompanied by written spells that would assure to them not only a life in the hereafter and protection from the dangers lurking there (as in the case of Spell 1034), but one in which, like the kings of old, they accompanied the solar god in his bark, talked to the gods, received their magical protection, and even identified themselves with them. Thus the deceased calls himself Shu, the father of the gods (see below, Spell 76, II,5), and even Re (see Spell 1034, where the deceased says in the beginning that he is a "dignitary of Re" and in the end that he is Re himself: "for I am Re, a greater god than you"), and in Spell 335 (IV,186) the deceased declares flatly that he is Re "at his first rising from the horizon".[2]

The ultimate achievement of transforming the deceased into gods is promised in the title at the end of Spell 290 (which I have not included in my extracts):

"The man shall be transformed into any god the man may wish to be transformed into."

More important for us in this chapter, the deceased absorbs the creative functions and might of the gods with whom he identifies himself. So, in the course of assuming the divine person of Shu, he becomes the creator of the Chaos-gods. The association of these gods with a chaos defined in terms of the negative characteristics of indefinite space, the formless Watery Abyss, darkness, and gloom (characteristics embraced by the Egyptian words: *ḥḥ*, *nw*, *kk*, and *tnmw*) gives us precious information concerning the age of the eight gods of Hermopolis associated with the chaos (Spells 76, 79-80). This Ogdoad of Hermopolis consisted of four pairs that embraced these negative characteristics. We also find evidence in these spells of other Hermopolitan doctrines such as the existence in primordial times of the Great Cackler who bore the primordial egg (see the document below, notes 6, 7, 11). It is perhaps no accident that the coffins that give us the material on the Chaos-gods are almost exclusively from el-Bersha, which was a necropolis associated with Hermopolis.[3] For the most part, however, the *Coffin Texts* contain doctrines that are of Heliopolitan origins, e.g., the autogenesis of the creator as the "Great One who created himself" (Spell 335, IV, 188) and as Khepri in the very meaning of his name and the consequential autogenesis of the deceased, raised on his throne "by means of myself, without a father and a mother contributing to me" (Spell 245). In the former spell the deceased also indicates that he is the one who created his [own] names and that he is "Lord of the Ennead" (IV,190). In another spell he says that he is the "one who originated in the Abyss, and see, the Chaos-gods came out to me....I fashioned myself at my will according to my desire" (Spell 714). We also see expressed the belief that the Lord of All had the form of a snake at the first stages of creation, i.e. when he accomplished his four deeds for mankind (Spell 1130). The description of these deeds is a brief but remarkable account of the creation for man of the very necessities of his life: air, water (for growing), equality of nature accompanied by the creator's injunction to do right (but coupled with the moral freedom of man to disobey that injunction, a freedom which unfortunately many men have exercised), and worship of the gods of the nomes.

In these spells are found both of the Heliopolitan views of the generation of Shu and Tefenet: from Atum's spittle (Spell 76, II,3-4) or as the result of Atum's masturbation (Spell 245). Further, the phoenix of Re is described as the form of Atum that came into being in the chaos, the latter in terms of the negative qualities deified in Hermopolis as the four pairs of the Ogdoad (Spell 76, II,4). We also see the common Heliopolitan doctrine that the gods were created from the sweat of the Lord of All, and mankind from the tears of his eye (Spell 1130, VII,464-65). In Spell 335 the cosmos, i.e. "what exists", is characterized in a gloss as being eternity and everlastingness, i.e. day and night. Thus eternal time is tied directly to the existent and presumably was created as an aspect thereof. Not only do we find the solar voyage as one of the objectives of life in the hereafter described in the spells, but we find a group of spells that constituted a *Book of Two Ways*, which appears to have been the earliest example of books that describe that voyage. It constitutes a kind of guide to the paths to take, with the highlights and dangers of the voyage described (see Spells 1030, 1034,

1035, 1131, 1136, 1146, and 1162). I mentioned this work above in Chapter Two and commented on the fact that it included a map of the two ways (Fig. II.28).

It is in the course of this voyage that we see a number of spells introduced to provide magical protection to the voyager, as for example Spell 1034, which was to help him against the danger of the *Aftet*-snakes. Spell 1146 presents a mysterious mansion, presumably one of the desirable objectives of the voyage, for it was a "place of excellent magic". Magic was blatantly in play in Spell 83, "to be said over the forepart of a lion[-charm] made from carnelian (?) or from the bone of a vulture, to be given to a man for his neck when he descends to the necropolis as a protection from the soul of Shu".

In describing the voyage, the spells mention the Field of Offerings, familiar to us from the *Pyramid Texts*. The mention of this field in Spell 1162 ties it with Osiris and Thoth; that is to say, the deceased will find himself there among the Followings of Osiris and Thoth. This suggests a location of the Field of Offerings in the Netherworld. Incidentally, though the main purpose of the spells was still to ensure for the deceased a celestial future with Re, as was that of the utterances in the *Pyramid Texts*, we find in the *Coffin Texts* increasing reference to Osiris, showing the apparent spread of Osirian ideas and cult. The practice of referring to the dead king as Osiris, which we noted in the *Pyramid Texts*, is extended to the nonroyal deceased in the *Coffin Texts*.

A final remark on the form of the spells is in order: titles are quite often included, as will be evident in some of the extracts I have given below: Spells 76, 335, 1030 (at the end), 1034 (at the end), 1130, 1162. The inclusion of a title was to become the rule in the spells of the *Book of the Dead*, as we shall see (Doc. II.3).

## Texts and Studies of the *Coffin Texts*

The earliest edition of the *Coffin Texts* was that of P. Lacau, "Textes religieux égyptiens," *Recueil de travaux relatifs à la philologie et à l'archéologie égyptiennes et assyriennes*, Vols. 26-37 (1904-15), partially reprinted in *Textes religieux égyptiens* (Paris, 1910). This publication was based on coffins from Cairo only.

It was completely superseded by the superb edition of A. de Buck, *The Egyptian Coffin Texts*, 7 vols. (Chicago, 1935-61). Included are 1185 spells. The texts from all the coffins are given in parallel, vertical columns. De Buck's text was translated into English by R. O. Faulkner, *The Ancient Egyptian Coffin Texts*, 3 vols. (Warminster, 1973-78).

Before the publication of Faulkner's work a study with a translation of and a commentary on those spells considered to be part of the *Book of Two Ways* was published by L. H. Lesko, *The Ancient Egyptian Book of Two Ways* (Berkeley/Los Angeles/London, 1972). See the earlier study of H. Schack-Schackenburg, *Das Buch von den Zwei Wegen des seligen Toten* (Leipzig, 1903).

## The English Translation

I owe much to the excellent translation of Faulkner mentioned above in the section on texts and studies. I do, however, occasionally depart from his work and I have added bracketed phrases when I thought they would clarify the text. The textual references embedded in the text between slant lines are of course to the edition of A. de Buck. It would be difficult to overpraise the clarity and usefulness of that work. It is obvious that I have only skimmed the cosmogonic and cosmological ideas from this extensive collection and the reader will surely find further study of it of great profit if he wishes to gain further knowledge of ancient Egyptian religious thought.

# Notes to the Introduction of Document II.2

1. The list of the coffins used by de Buck in his edition is given in the front of each volume.

2. Still of great interest are the comments of J. H. Breasted, *Development of Religion and Thought in Ancient Egypt* (New York, 1912; Harper Torchbook, 1959), pp. 274-75: "The hereafter to which these citizens of the Feudal Age [the Middle Kingdom] looked forward was...still largely celestial and Solar as in the Pyramid Age....There is the same identification with the Sun-god which we found in the Pyramid Texts. There is a chapter of 'Becoming Re-Atum,' and several of 'Becoming a Falcon.' The deceased, now no longer the king, as in the Pyramid Texts, says: 'I am the soul of the god, self-generator....I have become he. I am he before whom the sky is silent,...I have become the limbs of the god, self-generator. He has made me into his heart (understanding), he has fashioned me into his soul. I am one who has breathed (?) the form of him who fashioned me, the august god, self-generator, whose name the gods know not....He has made me into his heart, he has fashioned me into his soul, I was not born with a birth.' This identification of the deceased with

the Sun-god alternates with old pictures of the Solar destiny, involving only association with the Sun-god. There is a chapter of 'Ascending to the Sky to the Place where Re is,' another of 'Embarking in the Ship of Re when he has Gone to his Ka,' and a 'Chapter of Entering into the West among the Followers of Re Every Day.' When once there the dead man finds among his resources a chapter of 'Being the Scribe of Re.'"

3. One merely has to note the coffins used by de Buck in Spells 76, 79, and so on, to see the truth of this statement.

# Document II.2

## The *Coffin Texts*

### Spell 76

/II,1/ Going forth to the sky, going aboard the bark of Re, and becoming a living god. Oh you eight Chaos-gods who are in charge of the chambers of the sky, whom Shu has made from the efflux of his members, who tied together the ladder of Shu (or Atum), come and meet your father in me..., for I am he who created and made you just as I was created /II,2/ by your father Atum. I am weary because of the Supports-of-Shu since I [as Shu] lifted up my daughter Nut upon me so that I might give her to my father Atum in his boundaries (i.e. in his celestial regions); I have set Geb under my feet... /II,3/ .... Indeed I am Shu whom Atum created, from whom Re came into being. I was not fashioned in a womb, nor knit together in an egg. I was not conceived, but Atum /II,4/ spat me out in the saliva of his mouth along with my sister Tefenet....The phoenix of Re was the form of Atum which came into being in *ḥḥ* (indefinite space), in *nw* (the Watery Abyss), in *kk* (darkness), and in *tnmw* (gloom).[1] /II,5/ I am Shu, the father of the gods .... It was I who once again begot the Chaos-gods in *ḥḥ*, in *nw*, in /II,6/ *kk*, and in *tnmw*. I am indeed Shu who begot the gods. /II.7/ O you eight Chaos-gods whom I made from the efflux of my flesh, whose names Atum made when *nw* was created, on the day when Atum spoke in it with Nu /II,8/ in *ḥḥ*, in *tnmw*, and in *kk* ....

### Spell 79
/II,23/ O you eight Chaos-gods who came forth from Shu, whose names the flesh of Atum created /II,24/ in accordance with the words of Nu in *ḥḥ*, in *nw*, in *tnmw*, and in *kk*....[2]

### Spell 80
/II,27/ O you eight Chaos-gods, being Chaos-gods, who encircle the sky with your arms, /II,28/ who gather together the sky and earth for Geb, Shu fashioned you in *ḥḥ*, in *nw*, in *kk*, and in *tnmw*, and he allots you to Geb and Nut, for Shu is eternity and Tefenet is everlastingness[3] .... /II,32/ Thus said Atum: Tefenet is my living daughter, and she shall be with her brother Shu, whose name is 'The Living One'. Her name is Maat (Order or Righteousness)[4] .... /II,35/ .... Nu said to Atum: Kiss your daughter Maat, put her at your nose that your heart may live, for she will not be far from you. Maat is your daughter and your son is Shu, whose name is 'The Living One'. Eat of your daughter Maat (i.e., thrive on her); it is your son Shu who will raise you up [in the sky] ....

### Spell 83
/II,46/ To be said over the forepart of a lion[-charm] made from carnelian (?) or from the bone of a vulture, to be given to a man for his neck when he descends to the necropolis as a protection from the soul *(bʾ)* of Shu, so that he may have power over the winds of heaven /II,47/ .... As for anyone who knows this spell, he will not die again, his foes will not have power over him, no magic *(ḥkʾ)* will restrain him on earth forever....

## Spell 223

/III,208/ Spell for breathing air in god's land (i.e. the realm of the dead).[5] O Atum, give to N. (the deceased) this sweet air which is in your nostrils, for I am the egg which is in the Great Cackler.[6]...

## Spell 245

/III,334/ Hail to you who arises and comes into being in this your name of Khepri. This is what is said to you: ... See, I have come and I bring you adoration and purification in the Pure Land, because I am the seed of my conception [achieved] on your behalf by means of your mouth, /III,335/ which bore me for you by means of your grasp (fist) in passion (i.e. in the orgasm of masturbation) .... /III,36/ .... I have arisen [on] my throne by means of myself, without a father and a mother contributing to me (i.e. to my conception and birth) ....

## Spell 307

/IV,63/ .... I am the soul *(b3)* who created the Watery Abyss and made a place in god's land (i.e. the realm of the dead); [my] nest will not be seen nor [my] egg broken,[7] for I am the lord of those who are on high, and I have made a nest in the limits of the sky....

## Spell 335[8]

/IV,184/ Going out by day from god's land (i.e. the realm of the dead) [by] the revered N., deceased. My speech to you has come into being, Atum. /IV,186/ I was alone. I am Re at his first rising from the horizon. /IV,188/ I am the Great One who created himself. *Who is the Great One who created himself? He is Nu (i.e. the Watery Abyss).* [I am he] /IV,190/ who created his names, Lord of the Ennead. /IV,191/ *Who is he? He is*

*Atum who is in his sun disk (aten).* /IV,192/ Yesterday is mine and I know tomorrow .... /IV,194/ The warship of the gods is according to my command *(dd)* .... /IV,199/ I am the Great Phoenix who is in On (i.e. Heliopolis). *Who is he? He is Osiris.*[9] /IV,200/ As for me, I am the examiner of what exists. *Who is he? He is Osiris. As for what exists, it is eternity and everlastingness.* /IV,202/ *As for eternity, it is day. As for everlastingness, it is night* .... /IV,244/ I saw Re being born yesterday from the buttocks of the Celestial Cow[10] .... /IV,276/ I am his twin souls dwelling in his two progeny. *What does it mean? As for his twin souls dwelling in his two progeny, they are Osiris* /IV,278/ *when he entered into Djedut (Mendes) and found the soul of Re there, and they embraced.* /IV,280/ *They (or he) became his twin souls* ....

## Spell 714
/VI,343/ I am Nu the Sole One who has no equal and who was born on the great occasion of my flood when I came into being. I am the one who flew up and whose form is that of Djebenen who is in his egg.[11] I am the one who originated in the Abyss, and see, the Chaos-gods came out to me. /VI,344/ See, I am flourishing. I brought my body into being with my own might. I am the one who made myself. I fashioned myself at my will according to my desire. That which came forth from me was in my charge....

## Spell 1030
/VII,258/ See, its starry sky is in On, the sun-folk are in Kheraha because its thousands of souls are born, because their bandages are donned, because their oars are grasped.[12] /VII,259/ I will go with them aboard the

lotus-bark at the dockyard of the gods. I will take possession of the bark which has lotus leaves at both ends. I will ascend in her to the sky. /VII,260/ I will sail in her in the company of Re. I will sail in her with Megef-ib. /VII,261/ I will act as pilot in her to the polar region of the sky, to the stairway of the bark of Mercury *(Sbg)*. Spell for sailing in the great bark of Re.

### Spell 1034

/VII,278/ Upon your faces, you *Aftet*-snakes! Let me pass, /VII,279/ for I am a powerful one, Lord of Powerful Ones. I am a dignitary of Re, Lord of Maat, whom Edjo made. My protection is /VII,280/ the protection of Re. See, he has gone all around the Field of Offerings, which belongs to me, for I am Re, a greater god than you. /VII,281/ .... Guidance to the Paths of Rostau.[13]

### Spell 1035

/VII,282/ I have passed over the paths of Rostau on water and on land; these are the paths of Osiris and are in the limits of the sky. As for anyone who knows this spell for going down into them, he himself will be a god in the Following of Thoth .... /VII,283/ .... But as for him who does not know this spell for passing over these paths, he will be counted as having been taken by the infliction (?) of the [truly] dead, ordained as one who is nonexistent, who shall never have maat.[14]

### Spell 1130

/VII,461/ Utterance by him whose names are secret, the Lord of All (*lit.* Lord to the Limit) .... /VII,462/ Go in peace! I will relate to you the four (*var.* two) good deeds which my heart did for me when I was within the body of the Coiled One (i.e., I had the form of a snake) in order that wrong *(isft)* might be silenced (i.e., disorder or chaos be quieted). I have done four good deeds within the portal of the horizon.[15] I made the four winds /VII,463/ that everyone might breathe in his time (i.e. his lifetime). Such was my deed there (i.e. in the matter). I made the great [annual] flood so that the poor as well as the grandee might have power. Such was my deed in the matter. I made every man like his fellows /VII,464/ and I commanded them not to do wrong, but their hearts disobeyed what I had said. Such was my deed in the matter. I made their hearts not to forget the West by making god's-offerings to the regional gods. Such was my deed in the matter. I created the gods from my sweat /VII,465/ and mankind from the tears of my eye .... I shall sail correctly in my bark, for I am Lord of Waters (*var.* of Eternity) when crossing the sky. /VII,466/ .... Hu is with Heka felling that person over there who is ill-disposed toward me[16] ....

### Spell 1131

/VII,473/ .... "Keeper to the Double Doors of the Horizon When They are Locked on Behalf of the Gods"--this is the name of their keepers, which is in writing .... As for anyone who does not know what they say, he shall fall into the nets..../VII,474/ But anyone who knows what they say shall pass through them and he shall sit beside the Great God .... [and] he will never perish ....

### Spell 1136

/VII,481/ .... I have come here on the wind (*var.* the north-wind), for I am the leg(?) of Shu with which the

Abyss was filled .... Hu who speaks in darkness belongs to me[17]....

## Spell 1146

/VII,496/ The image of a mansion .... The place of a spirit (ʾḫ), the place of excellent magic (ḥkʾ) ....

## Spell 1162

/VII,506/ Spell for being in the Field of Offerings among the Following of Osiris and among the Following of Thoth every day. They will eat bread among the living. They will never die, breath being in their nostrils.

*{For the notes to this document, see page 445.}*

# Notes to Document II.2

1.　These are characteristics of the primordial watery space in which creation took place. They were personalized and paired with feminine counterparts to become the Ogdoad of Hermopolis. The fourth condition listed here is *tnmw*, which I have translated as "gloom". We have already seen in Chapter Two that Amun and his consort Amaunet sometimes constituted the fourth pair of the Ogdoad. This pair embraced the concept of invisibility. Notice here how these conditions of chaos are immersed in the Heliopolitan doctrines of creation, for we have just seen expressed here the presumably older doctrine of the creation of Shu and Tefenet from Atum's spittle. Atum is himself described as having come into being in the primordial chaos delineated in those negative terms of *nw*, *ḥḥ*, *kk*, and *tnmw*. At this point the Chaos-gods are said to have been created by Shu in the primordial darkness and waters, and indeed the important function of Shu is evident from the fact that he is called the father of the gods.

2.　Again it is stressed that Shu has created the Chaos-gods in the Chaos under the same four conditions mentioned in Spell 76. The flesh of Atum is here held to have created the names of the Chaos-gods.

3.　Here the Chaos-gods are the supporters of the sky. Presumably they are the so-called Supports-of-Shu, which lifted Nut to the sky and kept her aloft. Again we notice that Shu is said to have fashioned them in the primordial chaos described by the four negative conditions mentioned in the earlier spells. Shu is called here "eternity" (perhaps the long stretch of past time) and Tefenet "everlastingness" (perhaps the indefinitely long future), so that together they represent all time. In Spell 335, given below, a gloss identifies "what exists" (i.e. the cosmos) with "eternity and everlastingness". These two then are identified with "day" and "night". Here then there is some confusion concerning the role of "day" and "night" in the scheme of things. Presumably, at the end of each day an "eternity" has passed and the night represents the coming recreation of the successive elements of the future "everlastingness". Now the night obviously includes the period when chaos is present and the sun-god is overcoming chaos to recreate the cosmos of the day. I hardly need say we should not seek in "night" any notion of a mathematical limit separating "eternity" and "everlastingness".

4.   Here we see, mythologically expressed, two aspects of creation, that is, of the coming into being of the cosmos. By creating Shu, his son, as light and air, Atum has brought forth life, and by creating his sister Tefenet in her name of Maat, the great creator has substituted the essential rightness or order (m$^i$$^c$t) of the cosmos for the essential wrongness or disorder (isft) of the chaos (see below, Spell 1130, VII,462).

5.   Needless to say, the most important things for the deceased to have at his resurrection in the realm of the dead were the ability to breathe (hence the ceremony of the Opening of the Mouth) and the air to breathe. This spell, it was hoped, would provide the latter.

6.   I have described the Hermopolitan doctrine of the Great Cackler above in Chapter Two.

7.   Again, we see here possible vestiges of the Hermopolitan conception of a primeval egg, a doctrine I

have discussed above in Chapter Two.

8.    This is a long spell, of which I have included but a brief extract. The additions in italics are glosses added to certain coffins. In the glosses Osiris has been prominently inserted into what are clearly Heliopolitan doctrines. In the main text we may have a trace of the doctrine of the creative word in the second sentence where the deceased says that his speech to Atum has come into being.

9.    Both in this gloss and the next we find interpretations involving Osiris.

10.    This birth is shown pictorially in Fig. II.2a, where the solar bark is seen to emerge from between the back legs or buttocks of the celestial cow. Recall that the cow faces west and the bark moves across her stomach amidst the stars.

11.    Here is one more trace of the doctrine of the primordial egg which was discussed in Chapter Two. It appears here mixed with Heliopolitan ideas.

12.    This is a picturesque account of the gods, and of the newly deceased in their bandages, i.e. embalmed, boarding the solar bark at the dockyard of the gods in the district of Heliopolis known as Kheraha (see Doc. I.1, n. 114). Recall that the thousands of stars, which, by euphemism, become the starry sky, are thought of either as the gods or as the habitations of the gods. At any rate, here the gods and the deceased, as they board the bark, take up their oars. There is a nice bit of detail in the passage in which the bark is described as being shaped in the form of lotus leaves at both ends.

13.    This is a rubric or title that appears more appropriate for the next spell. I have already mentioned in Chapter Two that the earliest view of the location of

Rostau was that it was near or at the necropolis of Saqqara.

14. This is good evidence for the view held by some Egyptians that if the traveler loses his way and does not find the true path, he becomes truly dead, that is, he is in the state of the nonexistent, and one who is nonexistent is one who never will experience maat. In short, he is a part not of the order of the cosmos but rather of the disorder of chaos. I have discussed these various ideas briefly in Chapter Two above.

15. Here the Lord of All gives a remarkable account of what he has done for man by outlining four deeds. In the first place he created the winds that man might be able to breathe. Then he created the annual floods which make the growing of crops so easy that the poor can be sustained as well as the rich. Thirdly, he made every one like his fellows and commanded or perhaps instructed them not to do wrong. However, the great god confesses, men's hearts have led them to disobey him. Hence we seem to have a doctrine of man's moral freedom expressed here.

16. I have already mentioned in Chapter Two that Hū (the personified authoritative or creative command) and Sia (personified creative intelligence) were often found accompanying the solar god in his bark, and that on occasion Heka (personified magical power) appeared instead of Hu (see above, Chapter Two, note 44). Now here we have a case where Hu and Heka (presumably in the bark with the deceased) are together protecting the solar god from some one who is hostile to him.

17. This is probably a veiled reference to Hu as the creative word working in the primordial darkness. Thus, the deceased, by identifying himself with Hu, that

is, by claiming that Hu (creative word) belongs to him, hopes to absorb some of the powers of the creator gods.

# Document II.3: Introduction

## The *Book of the Dead*

The third stage of the development of funerary documents in ancient Egypt is represented by the collections on papyrus of spells that are known by the title of *Book of the Dead.* Though there is no single Egyptian title for the various versions of the collections, the title most often found is *Spells for Going Forth by Day,* a title that indicates that a main purpose of the spells was to allow the deceased to leave the tomb in any form in which he wished to leave it. As one can readily see by examining the editions and the translations listed below, there is no single canonical collection. Each collection was commissioned or simply bought already prepared for a particular deceased, and each collection contained whatever number of spells was thought desirable and affordable.

The practice of making these collections on papyrus so that the papyrus could be placed in the tomb of the deceased began in the eighteenth dynasty, though the spells themselves were often modified versions of those already used on the coffins of the Middle Kingdom. Just as the number of spells was by no means fixed, so the order of the spells (and thus their ordinal number) was not always precisely fixed, though there was a generally accepted order later. However, since the beginning of the editing of these collections by Lepsius in the middle of the nineteenth century, a general system of numbering has been assumed by the scholars working on this material. Lepsius numbered 165 spells and in Allen's recent translation (see the bibliographic section below) we find the numbers extended to Spell 192 plus Pleyte Spells 166-74. These numbers are not truly indicative of the great variety that exists among the versions, for many spells occur in diverse forms. For example, Spell 15 exists in fourteen different versions, and these versions themselves vary in length and thus in richness of content. One can get a better sense of the complexity of the situation by going through Allen's translation carefully, since he tells us the sources and their dates for each of the variant versions.

Allen's remarks about the general history of the collections are pertinent:[1]

> The content and length of any given Book of the Dead depend on various factors: quantity and quality of scribes and spells available, wealth of the deceased, local usage, etc. During the Empire, only a few spells had begun to occur together in small groups, and to find any two manuscripts of exactly similar layout would be unusual. Before Ptolemaic times, however, perhaps by the fifth century B.C., a definite set of spells in a definite order had become fairly standard. In 1842 the great German Egyptologist Richard Lepsius published in facsimile a late Ptolemaic document of this type belonging to the Turin Museum. The

numbers he assigned to its successive spells are those which we still use, plus further numbers for spells there absent but found elsewhere and added by William Pleyte, Édouard Naville, E. A. Wallis Budge, and the present writer.

The present volume deals with all the spells yet numbered, which total 192, plus some insertions. In following the established order we vary widely, of course, from the diverse orders found within the documents themselves, for the texts here translated are those of the Empire rather than later times whenever available. Even so, earlier versions of many spells occur. All but 79 have a Middle Kingdom background in the Coffin Texts, written mostly on the insides of wooden coffins of the 19th or 20th century B.C. A few even go back to the Pyramid Texts of the 23rd or 24th century B.C., composed then or even earlier and used in the Old Kingdom for royalty alone.

In choosing the extracts given below, I have attempted to illustrate some of the more important cosmogonical and cosmological doctrines which I have discussed in Chapter Two. I have also given a good example of a spell in the *Book of the Dead* (Spell 17) which had its origin in the *Coffin Texts* (Spell 335). Comparison of the two will illustrate the types of changes made. It will also show how the glosses began to expand, so that virtually nothing of the past was abandoned when something new was added.

The same doctrinal tendencies that we saw in the earlier funerary material are still present in the *Book of the Dead*,[2] such as the great importance of the solar god and his creative activities (see below, Spells 15*A*3, 15*A*4, 15*B* 1, 15*B* 2, 15*B* 2 variant, 17); the vestiges of Hermopolitan concepts like the Lake of the Twin Knives (Spell 15*A*3), the Isle of Flame (Spell 15*B* 1), the emergence of the young sun from the primordial lotus (*ibid.*), the birth of Shu (as light) on the primitive hill of Hermopolis (Spell 17), and the primordial egg and the Great Cackler (Spells 54, 56); and further elaboration of the hereafter but with emphasis on Osiris in the Netherworld (Spell 175 and Spell 30*A* [note 3 below]), the Osirian judgment at the Hall of the Two Truths (Spell 125 and Spell 30*A* [again see note 3 below]), and accounts of the Fields of Offerings and of Rushes (apparently by this time a part of Osiris's realm in the Netherworld) which describe the familiar agricultural and pleasurable activities that the deceased had enjoyed before death and burial (Spells 99, 110).

One remarkable spell (175) recounts a conversation between Atum and Osiris. Osiris complains about the conditions of the Netherworld (too silent, no water, no air, very deep, very dark, no sexual pleasures), and Atum offers Osiris in recompense blessedness, quietness of heart, the earthly throne for his son Horus, and above all survival along with Atum at the end of time when Atum will destroy everything he made at the time of creation, i.e. everything and everybody that make up the cosmos except Osiris and himself, and even he (Atum) will return to his primitive serpent-forms.

In one of the most important and well-known spells (Spell 125) we see the wholesale elaboration of an earlier tendency to declare in a tomb biography the freedom of the deceased from wrongdoing. In the deceased's denial of a long list of sinful actions, we see clearly what constituted the proper code of conduct at the time of the New Kingdom. The importance of this for our cosmological study is simply that the creator not only set out maat or order for the cosmos but simultaneously set out with it maat or truth for individuals, i.e. right conduct. It would of course be surprising if very many people of power could truly assert that they had led the blameless life outlined in Spell 125. Indeed there is evident recognition among the Egyptians of the fact that men will often say anything to achieve resurrection in the Netherworld, for there exists a spell whose purpose is to make sure that the deceased's heart does not speak out against him in god's domain.[3] But perhaps they thought that if the statements of innocence were solemnly and formally spoken as a spell, then by the doctrine of the creative word, i.e. the bringing into existence of something by magical word, the assertion could somehow produce the truth. We are reminded that this doctrine is evident in Spell 17, when at the very beginning it is said "My words come to pass" (*ḫpr*, lit., "are created").

I mentioned in the introduction to Document II.2 that the spells began to acquire titles in the Middle Kingdom, titles often written in red ink. These rubrics multiplied as time went on, so that most of the spells of the various versions of the *Book of the Dead* had their special titles. Allen distinguishes the preliminary materials connected with titles from the spells proper by using a marginal P for the preliminary material and a marginal S for the spells themselves. On occasion there are also separately distinguishable terminal comments, which Allen identifies with a marginal T.

### Texts and Studies of the *Book of the Dead*

The earliest edition of any version of the *Book of the Dead* was that of C. R. Lepsius, *Das Todtenbuch der Ägypter nach dem hieroglyphischen Papyrus in Turin* (Turin and Leipzig, 1842; repr. Osnabruck, 1969). The papyrus produced in facsimile in Lepsius's work dated from Ptolemaic times and thus contained material not in the earlier versions.

Almost a half-century later E. Naville produced the standard version of the text: *Das ägyptische Todtenbuch der XVII. bis XX. Dynastie aus verschiedenen Urkunden zusammengestellt und herausgegeben*, 3 vols. (Berlin, 1886). This text includes the pictorial vignettes found in various manuscripts.

Convenient, too, is the text produced by E.A.W. Budge, *The Chapters of Coming Forth by Day or the Theban Version of the Book of the Dead. The Egyptian Hieroglyphic Text Edited from Numerous Papyri*, 3 vols. (London, 1910). Budge also prepared a now-out-of-date English translation: *The Book of the Dead. An English Translation of the Chapters, Hymns, etc., of the Theban Recension*, 2nd ed., rev. and enl., 3 vols. (London, 1909).

See the selected spells edited by H. Grapow, *Religiöse Urkunden (Urkunden des ägyptischen Altertumskunde, Abt. V)*, 3 Heften (Leipzig, 1915-17).

By far the most important of the recent studies and translations are those of T.G. Allen: *The Egyptian*

*Book of the Dead. Documents in the Oriental Institute Museum at the University of Chicago (The University of Chicago Oriental Institute Publications,* Vol. 82) (Chicago, 1969), and *The Book of the Dead or Going Forth by Day. Ideas of the Ancient Egyptians Concerning the Hereafter as Expressed in Their Own Terms (The Oriental Institute of the University of Chicago Studies in Ancient Oriental Civilization,* No. 37) (Chicago, 1974).

Also useful (but not nearly so comprehensive as Allen's translation) is the translation by R. O. Faulkner, *The Ancient Egyptian Book of the Dead,* revised edition by C. Andrews (London, 1985). This revision contains beautiful reproductions of numerous vignettes. Miss Andrews has translated some spells and parts of spells omitted in the earlier edition of Faulkner's translation published by the Limited Editions Club in New York, 1972 (see Bibliography below).

## The English Translation

I have followed Allen's translation with little change, except to keep my earlier translations of some of the doctrinal terms, like "eternity" for *nḥḥ* and "everlastingness" for *ḏt*. I have also retained the marginal letters and numbers used by Allen, which appear here as bold-faced letters at the beginning of the sections they mark. As in the case of my extracts from Documents II.1 and II.2, the extracts for this third document present only a pale picture of the whole complex structure of the various versions of the *Book of the Dead.*

# Notes to the Introduction of Document II.3

1. See the translation by Allen, *The Book of the Dead*, pp. 1-2.

2. For a brief but illuminating description and comparison of the spells of both the *Coffin Texts* and the *Book of the Dead*, treated together as one form of funerary texts, see H. Kees, "Toten-Literatur," *Handbuch der Orientalistik*, Abt. 1, Vol. 1, Part 2, pp. 61-69.

3. See Allen, *The Book of the Dead*, Spell 30*A*, p. 40: "Spell for not letting N.'s heart oppose him in the god's domain. He says: My heart of my mother, my heart of my mother, my breast that I had on earth, stand not against me as a witness before the Lords of Offerings. Say not against me 'He really did it' concerning what I have done. Bring no charges against me before the great god the lord of the west (i.e. Osiris)." I have not included this spell in my extracts below.

# Document II.3

## The *Book of the Dead*

### Spell 15A3[1]

*a*

/**P**,l/ Adoring Re as he rises in the eastern horizon of the sky. /2/ Osiris N. shall say:

/**S**,l/ Hail to thee, Re at his rising, Atum at his setting.[2] Thou risest, thou risest, thou shinest, thou shinest, having dawned as king of the gods. /2/ Thou art lord of the sky and earth, who made the stars above and mankind below, sole god who came into being at the beginning of time, who made the lands and created common people, who made the deep *(nw)* [3] and created the inundation, who made the water and gave life to what is in it, who fashioned the mountains and brought into being man and beast. /3/ Sky and earth greet thee with libations; Truth *(M³ᶜt)* embraces thee day and night. /4/ Thou traversest the sky in gladness, the Lake of the Twin Knives having grown calm.... /6/ (As for) him who is in his shrine, his heart is pleased, for he has dawned as dominator of the sky, sole one, keen, who came forth from the deep, Re triumphant, divine youth, heir of eternity *(nḥḥ)* [4] who begot himself and bore himself, sole one, great in number of forms, King of the Two Lands, Ruler of Heliopolis, lord of eternity, familiar with everlastingness *(dt)*. /7/ The Ennead is in joy over thy rising. (They) who are in the horizon paddle (thee); (they) who are in the night bark exalt thee....

*b*

/**S**,3/ No tongue could understand its fellow except for thee alone....

## Spell 15*A*4[5]

/**P**/ Adoring Re at his rising in the eastern horizon of the sky.

/**S**,1/ Hail to (thee) child in ⌐the ⌐same way as yesterday⌐,[6] rising from the lotus, goodly youth who has ascended from the horizon and illumines [the ⌐Two⌐ Land⌐s⌐ with] his light....

## Spell 15*B* 1[7]

*b*

/**S**,2/ (Then) I shall see the great god who lives yonder in the Isle of Flame, the youth (born) of gold who came forth from the lotus....[8]

## Spell 15*B* 2[9]

/**S**,1/ Hail to thee Re [maker of] all mankind, Atum-Harakhti, sole god, living on truth, maker of what is and creator of what exists of animals and human beings that came forth from his eye, lord of the sky and earth, maker of mankind below and (the stars) above, Lord of the Universe, bull of the Ennead,[10] King of the sky, lord of the gods, Sovereign at the head of the Ennead, divine God who came into being of himself, Primeval One, who came into being at the beginning....

## Spell 15*B* 2 variant[11]

/**S**,2/ Joy to thee, maker of the gods, who lifted high the sky to be the pathway of his eyes,[12] who made the earth to be the broad realm of his Sunlight, that every man might perceive his fellow....

### Spell 17[13] (*cf.* Doc. II.2, Spell 335)

*a*

/**P**,3/ (Spell for) going forth by day, assuming whatever form one will, playing senet, sitting in a pavilion, going forth as a living soul by N., after he moors (i.e. dies).[14]

/**S**,1/ My words come to pass. ⟨All[15] was⟩ mine when [I] existed in the Deep; (I was) Re at ⟨his⟩ dawnings when he began his reign.

> What does it mean, that is "Re when he began his reign"? It means when Re began dawning in the kingdom he had created before the uplifting of Shu had come into being, while ⟨he was on⟩ the hill that was in Hermopolis. Now the children [of the feeble one] had been given ⌈with⌉ them that were in Hermopolis.

/2/ I am the great god who came into being of himself,

> Who is he, "the [great] god who came into being of himself"? (He is) water; he is the Deep (i.e. *Nw*), the Father of the gods. Variant: He is Re.

who created himself, lord ⟨of the Ennead⟩,

> Who is he? He is Re when he created the names of his members. So came into being these gods who are in his Following.

(most) irresistible of gods.

> Who is he? He is Atum who is in his Disk. [Variant:] He is Re when he rises from the eastern horizon of the sky.

/3/ Mine is yesterday, and I know tomorrow.

> Who is He? "Yesterday" is Osiris; "tomorrow" is Re. That is the day when the

enemies of the Lord of the Universe were annihilated and his son Horus was caused to reign. Variant: That is the day of the Festival (called) We Abide, that is (the day) when the burial of Osiris was directed by his Father ⟨Re⟩ ....

/5/ I am this (great) phoenix that is in Heliopolis, the examiner of what exists.

Who is he? He is Osiris. As for "what exists", (that means) the great god. Variant: it means eternity and everlastingness. As for "eternity", that is day; as for "everlastingness", that is night...

## Spell 42[16]

/P,l/ Spell for warding off the harm that is done in Heracleopolis....

/S,2/ My hair is (that of) the Deep; my face is (that of) the Disk. My eyes are (those of) Hathor; my ears are (those of) Wepwawet. My nose is (that of) the Presider over ⌐Xois⌐; my lips are (those of) Anubis [and so on through other parts of the body] .... /4/ I am one who has ascended sound, whose name [is not known]. I am yesterday; my [name] is He Who Sees a Million Years, who has gone, who has gone along the roads of the Chief Examiners. [I am lord of everlastingness .... /5/ I am your protector for millions ⌐(of years)⌐ .... I shall not die again.... /6/ .... I am the blossom that came forth from the Deep, and Nut is my mother, O thou who didst create me, I am one who strides not, the great commander within yesterday, the commander's portion being within my hand. There is none that knows me or shall know me; there is none who grasps me or shall grasp me. O thou of the egg, thou of the egg, I am

Horus presiding over millions ....

## Spell 54[17]

/P,1/ Spell for giving breath to N. in the god's domain.
/S,1/ O Atum, give me the refreshing breath that is in my nose. I am this egg that was in the Great Cackler. (I am) this great magical protection that came into being and separated Geb from the earth. If I live, it lives; if I grow old, it (grows old). If I breathe air, (it breathes air) ....

## Spell 56[18]

/S,1/ O Atum, mayest thou give me the refreshing breath that is in thy nose. It is I who occupy this (great) seat in the midst of Hermopolis. I have guarded this egg of the Great Cackler. If I flourish, it flourishes. If I live, it lives; if I breathe air, it breathes air....

## Spell 99[19]
c

/S,3/ .... Your offerings to me are barley and wheat; your offerings to me (are) myrrh and clothing. (Your) offerings to me (are) oxen and fowl; (your) offerings to me (are) life, soundness, and health. Your offerings to me (include the right) to go forth (by) day in any form in which I may wish to go forth (from) the Field of Rushes.
/T/ If one recites this spell, he goes forth (by) day from the Field (of Rushes). Given him are a cake, a jar, a *pz(n)*-loaf, a chunk of meat, and (fields of) barley and ⌜Upper Egyptian⌝ wheat 7 cubits (high). It is the Followers of Horus who reap them for him. Then he shall chew (on) this barley and wheat and shall wipe his body therewith, and his body shall be as (those of)

these gods. (So) he goes forth from the Field of Rushes in any form in which he may wish to go forth.

/T var. 2/ A truly excellent spell (proved) a million times.

## Spell 110[20]

### *a* 1

/P,1/ Beginning of the spells for the Field of Offerings, the spells for going forth by day, going in and out of the god's domain, attaining the Field of Rushes, existing in the Field of Offerings, the great settlement, ... gaining control there, becoming a blessed one there, plowing there, reaping (there), eating there, drinking there, copulating there, doing everything that is done upon earth....

/S,2/ Lo, I paddle (in) this great bark in the lake(s) of Hotep; it is I who took it (i.e. the bark) from ⌐the limbs⌐ of Shu. (His) limbs and his stars are ⌐years and seasons⌐ .... /3/ I prevail over her (i.e. the field), (for) I am the one who knows her. I paddle in her lake(s), so that I arrive at her settlements. My mouth becomes powerful, and I become sharper than the blessed .... I become a blessed one therein; I eat (there)in, I drink therein. I plow therein, I reap therein, I grind therein. I copulate therein; my ⟨magic⟩ becomes powerful therein ....

## Spell 125[21]

### *a*

/P/ What to say on arriving at the broad hall of the Two Truths, cutting N. off from all the forbidden things he has done, and seeing the faces of all the gods....

/S,2/ I have not sinned against anyone. I have not mistreated people. I have not done evil instead of righteousness. I know not what is not (i.e. the nonexistent); I have not done anything bad.... I have not reviled the god. I have not laid violent hands on an orphan. I have not done what the god abominates. I have not slandered a servant to his superior. I have not made (anyone) grieve; I have not made (anyone) weep. I have not killed; I have not turned (anyone) over to a killer; I have not caused anyone's suffering. I have not diminished the food(-offerings) in the temples. I have not debased the offering-cakes of the gods. I have not taken the cakes of the blessed. I have not copulated (illicitly); I have not been unchaste. I have not increased or diminished the measure, I have not diminished the palm(-measure); I have not encroached upon fields. I have not added to the balance weights; I have not tampered with the plumb bob of the balance....

*c*

/S,6/ I (have) purified myself in the southern site. I have gone to rest in the northern settlement, (in) the field of grasshoppers wherein I purify myself at this hour of night or day (for soothing the hearts of the gods when I pass through it by night or by day). "Let him come," say they of me. "Who art thou?" say they to me. "What is thy name?" say they to me. I am the lord of the undergrowth (of) a papyrus clump; He Who is in the Moringa is my name. "What did(st thou) pass through?" say they to me. I passed through a settlement north of a thicket.... [With further answers given correctly, the guardians say] "Come thou, enter through this gate of (this) broad hall of the Two Truths, for thou knowest us." [Similar inquisitions follow, in which the deceased has to produce the names of the jambs of the gates, the leaves of the gate, the floor of the gate, and so on.][22]

## Spell 175[23]

*b*

/P/ To be said by Osiris N.:

/S,l/ O Atum, what means it that I proceed to the necropolis, the silent land, which has no water and no air and is very deep and very dark and (all) is lacking, wherein one lives in quietness of heart and without any sexual pleasures available? "I have given blessedness instead of water, air, and sexual pleasure, quietness of heart instead of bread and beer", says Atum.... (But) every (other) god has mounted his throne in <the bark of> millions (of years). "Thy throne (belongs) to thy son Horus", says Atum .... /2/ "What is a lifetime of life?" says (Osiris). "Thou art (destined) for millions of millions (of years), a lifetime of millions (of years).... And [then] I will destroy all that I have made. This land shall return into the Deep, into the flood, as it was aforetime. (Only) I shall survive together with Osiris, after I have assumed my forms of other (snakes) which men know not and gods see not...."

# Notes to Document II.3

1. This is based on a 19th-dynasty papyrus (Ag in Allen's list).

2. This is a variation of the usual formula: the solar god is called Khepri at rising, Re in midday, and Atum in the evening. I have retained here Allen's respectful forms in using his translation of this hymn to Re.

3. Allen usually translates *nw* as "deep", while ordinarily I have translated it by "Abyss". This is somewhat different from the usual statement that Atum created himself in the Abyss, for here we have him creating it.

4. I stick with my previous translations of *nḥḥ* and *ḏt* by "eternity" and "everlastingness". Allen translates them by "perpetuity" and "eternity". As I have noted before, the two words together constitute eternal time as an aspect of creation, i.e. of the cosmos.

5. This version is found in Papyrus Ba in Allen's list (also of the 19th dynasty).

6. This is one of the sections that mention the Hermopolitan doctrine of the sun's emergence from a lotus blossom as a "goodly youth".

7. This version was also found in Papyrus Ba from Allen's list.

8. Two Hermopolitan doctrines are mentioned here: the Isle of Flame or Fire and the primordial lotus blossom.

9. This spell is known from two documents: one from the 18th and one from the 19th dynasty. See Allen's translation. Notice the allusion to mankind's creation from the eye of Re, needless to say from his

tears.

10. The expression "bull of the Ennead" simply means that Re is the progenitor of the Ennead. This title is coupled with the usual epithets of a creator god.

11. From the 19th-dynasty papyrus Da in Allen's list.

12. This is no doubt a reference to the sun-disk and the moon-disk. The statement that follows is the usual one that says that Re created his light in order that man might see.

13. This is based largely on Aa of the 18th dynasty but was restored or added to from Papyrus Ce and occasionally from the version in Spell 335 of the *Coffin Texts*. I have included this spell so that the reader may compare the two versions. I have found it useful to consult the edition of this spell constructed by Grapow from versions of it ranging from the time of the Middle Kingdom through the Late Period (see the text noted above in the introduction to the document).

14. I have included only part of the preliminary material; for the rest of it (i.e. for sections /P,1/ and /P,2/), see Allen's translation. For the vignettes which show the deceased in a pavilion playing senet, see Fig. II.26.

15. In some versions of Spell 335 of the *Coffin Texts*, the *tm* here rendered as "All" was read as "Atum" and was attached to the preceding sentence.

16. Based on two versions of the 18th dynasty (see Allen's translation). The deceased's effort to become a god reflects the similar objective of the part-by-part identification of the deceased with gods which was found in the *Pyramid Texts* (Doc. II.1, Sects. 1303-05). Again note traces of Hermopolitan doctrines in this spell.

17. Based on 18th-dynasty papyri (see Allen's translation). Allen calls the Great Cackler "the Great Honker". This and the next extract (Spell 56) demonstrate the continued interest in the Hermopolitan doctrine of the Great Cackler which was present in the *Coffin Texts*.

18. This spell is from 18th-dynasty papyri (see the translation of Allen). It specifically ties the doctrine of the Great Cackler to Hermopolis.

19. From the 18th dynasty. See Allen's translation. In Chapter Two, I have commented on the details given here concerning the agricultural benefits of being in the Field of Rushes.

20. More details on the good life followed in the Field of Rushes in this spell found in 18th-dynasty papyri (see Allen's translation). This chapter attracted pictorial vignettes (see Figs. II.25-26).

21. This spell from 18th-dynasty papyri (see Allen's translation) is one of the most celebrated of all spells in the *Book of the Dead*. There are two versions of the somewhat misnamed "Negative confession", i.e. lists of sins or wrongful acts which the deceased affirms that he has not committed. I have given much of the shorter list. For the longer list, see Allen's translation, part *b*.

22. The reader will notice here just one more instance of the importance of knowing names for achieving desirable objectives. It is a part of the ancient Egyptian interest in magical words that persisted from the very beginning of their written literature. I have often commented on this in Chapter Two above and have particularly stressed the significance of it for the doctrine of the creative word.

23. Based on both 18th- and 19th-dynasty copies

# ANCIENT EGYPTIAN SCIENCE

(see Allen's translation). In Chapter Two I mentioned the importance of this spell for the doctrine of the cessation of the cosmos and the return to the condition of chaos that existed prior to creation.

# Document II.4: Introduction

## The *Book of Amduat*

The *Book of Amduat* or *Amdat*, which may be translated as the *Book of What Is in the Netherworld*, is one of several works whose earliest copies appear in the tombs of the kings of the New Kingdom. Two other significant works of a similar nature are the *Book of Gates* and the *Book of Caverns*. Though we know nothing about the origins of these works, we can suppose on the basis of extant copies that the *Amduat* is the earliest of them.

I have given a brief account of the *Amduat* in Chapter Two, but certain other details ought to be mentioned here. In the first place, it exists in two versions, a discursive one that is long and a poetic one that is short. Both of the versions are found in the tombs of the kings in the Valley of the Kings in Western Thebes, sometimes the shorter version following at the end of the longer one. The extracts given here are from the long version. Its earliest extant copy is fragmentary and from the tomb of Tuthmosis I (1504-1491 B.C.). The copy on the walls of the tomb of his grandson Amenhotep II is the most complete. Details of the various other copies from the New Kingdom, some of which are in the tombs of nobles (in fact the second-earliest copy is found in the tomb of the vizier Weseramon in the time of Tuthmosis III, where also is found the earliest copy of the short version), are given in the edition of Hornung mentioned below.

The name by which this work is known, *t<sup>ꜣ</sup> md<sup>ꜣ</sup>t imit dw<sup>ꜣ</sup>t*, is one sometimes applied generally to such underworld-books, and indeed it appears in some later copies of this work.[1] The title given in the earliest version is that which we have included in the extracts below, "The Writing of the Hidden Place (or Chamber)". This is followed by a kind of table of contents of what is included in the work: the locations and activities of the various souls, gods, and shades that occupy the twelve hours or regions of the Netherworld, the speeches of Re to them, the various gates, the course of the hours and their gods, and so on. When we first see this book in the tombs of the kings, it clearly has become a substantial element of the royal (and occasionally noble) funerary literature. The major objective of placing the book in the royal tomb is to ensure the king's rebirth like that of his father Re. There are passages in it that also have a ritual significance, as for example in the introduction to the second hour where we read that offerings will be made on earth in the names of the gods of this region. They will be effective for the celebrant on earth, "as has been proved true a million times".

In the royal tombs the work is laid out on the walls like a gigantic papyrus. It is divided into twelve sections, each representing one of the hours of the night, and it is organized about paintings in each section (see Figs. II.29-40). The character of the work is epitomized by Piankoff in the following way:[2]

> The *Book of Am-Duat* or *Book of What Is in the Netherworld*, is a composition very similar to the *Book of Gates*. It contains twelve

divisions...,each division (except the introductory division) is formed of three registers, the sun barge being in the central one. But there are no gates [depicted], and each division is usually preceded by a short introduction giving the name of the hour. In the *Book of Gates* the barge is the same in all twelve divisions; in the *Book of Am-Duat*, however, the number of the crew and the aspect of the barge change in almost every division. The crew is usually composed of the Opener of the Ways [Wepwawet], Mind [Sia], Mistress of the Barge, [Re, i.e. Flesh of Re,] Horus the Praiser, the Bull of Truth, the Watchful One, Will [Hu], and the Guide of the Barge. In the second division Isis and Nephthys also appear on the barge, in the shape of two serpents. In the first division the prow of the barge is covered by a mat of reeds. In the second, sixth, and all other divisions with the exception of the fourth and fifth, the prow and the stern both terminate in a lotus flower. In the eleventh division a disk rests on the lotus flower of the prow; in the twelfth a scarab. In divisions four and five the prow and the stern of the barge both terminate in the head of a serpent. The bow is towed in divisions four,

five, eight, and twelve. The serpent
which envelops the god appears only
from the seventh division on. In the
second and third divisions the barge
is seen in the great waters, in all
others it is placed on a small section
marked as water.

As Piankoff notes, this description applies to the older,
more traditional versions of the book.

Though, as I have said, the work was clearly a
funerary work by the time of its earliest known copy
from the tomb of Tuthmosis I, there is some reason to
believe that it may have originated as an early
topography of, and a guide to, the Netherworld,
modeled after works like the Onomastica that describe
the entities of this world. This seems to be borne out
by the initial table of contents and by the fact that at
each hour the work catalogues the peculiar features of
the region and the inhabitants of that hour.
Furthermore, the insistence again and again that the
gods represented are "like this in the Netherworld"
seems to reflect a style that emphasizes the veracity of
accounts, a style that seems to give the book a
quasi-scientific or empirical air of the sort found in the
Edwin Smith Surgical Papyrus, which we shall study in
Chapter Five of Volume Three.

Altenmüller has suggested that the work may go
back to the fourth or fifth dynasty,[3] a time when some
sort of medical works like the surgical papyrus seem to
have been composed. Whether such speculations are
true or not, the purpose of the inclusion of this
document in my account is to give the reader some idea
of standard views of the Otherworld in the New
Kingdom. I have also included it to show the

persistence of the cosmogonic and cosmological ideas in works other than collections of spells or hymns.

Generally the cosmogonic ideas represented in the *Book of Amduat* are those associated with the Heliopolitan system and its modifications by the time of the growing dominance of Amon-Re. The whole drama confirms the primacy of the creation of Re by himself as Khepri. It surely is significant that in the second register of the twelfth hour Re is towed through the body of a snake and "comes out of its mouth, being born in his forms of Khepri, and of the gods who are in his bark as well". Hence as the creator creates his new emergent forms of Khepri he also creates the forms of the other gods of his crew as forms of himself. Presumably the same kind of creation by the multiplication of his forms took place when he brought the Ennead into creation, though he seems to say in the first register of the fifth hour that such a creation of forms took place after the creation of their bodies: "May you breathe, O Ennead of gods, who came into being from my flesh when your forms were not yet created."

The comparison of the rebirth of Re with the birth process of the beetle as he pushes his egg along is alluded to in the first register of the tenth hour when we are told that the gods of the Cavern of the West ("where Khepri rests with Re") are "in the forms and births of Khepri when he carries his egg toward this city in order to come forth afterwards in the Eastern Horizon of Heaven". As we have seen, snake forms like that of Neheb-kau ("The Provider of Forms") were important in the early stages of creation, and that importance is reflected throughout this book, particularly in the last hours of the night that precede the actual rebirth of Re.

But following his self-generation the creator god created the gods and mankind. That role of creation is reflected in this work by continual references to his gift of life and breath to all the gods and spirits of the Netherworld. For example, in the third register of the second hour, the gods who have already confirmed his lordship of time by presenting him with year- and age-signs are said to "live through the voice of this Great God. Their throats breathe when he calls them and assigns them their duties." Clearly the doctrine of the creative word that is a part of the Heliopolitan system in the form of the divinities Sia and Hu as personalized Conception and Command is evident in the temporary revivification of the underworld gods when they hear Re's voice each night. Indeed I have stressed here and in the notes below the fact that Sia and Hu accompany the solar god as part of the crew of his bark, Heka (Magic) being substituted for Hu in one instance (see Doc. II.4, notes 2 and 4). The importance of magical utterances is stressed in the second register of the seventh hour where we read that the solar bark "is towed by the magical utterances of Isis and the Elder Magician". But here the reference is not so much to creative words as it is to destructive ones, since the purpose of the magic of Isis and the Elder Magician is to fend off the serpent Neha-her or the serpent Apep.

The pre-existent Abyss from which the Great God brought himself into being lurks everywhere in the Netherworld of this book and it is seen to constitute a constant danger to the creator god. Similarly, those creatures of the Abyss, the nonexistent ones, are said, in the third register of the third hour, to be annihilated by the gods of that hour, and it is the nonexistent ones who live in a special "Place of Annihilation-houses".

It is also abundantly clear from the *Amduat* that the concept of the birth and death of gods has been significantly elaborated beyond (1) the earlier Heliopolitan idea of successive generations of gods, starting with Atum, then proceeding to his children Shu and Tefenet, then to Geb and Nut, followed by their children Osiris, Isis, Seth and Nephthys, and then to Horus, the son of Osiris and Isis: in all, five generations; and (2) the death of Osiris and his resurrection in the Netherworld. Now we find mentioned in this work not only the corpse of Osiris (second register of the fifth hour), but also those of Sokar and Khepri himself. In the fifth hour we see Sokar's head sticking out from his pyramidal burial mound of sand, while the body of Khepri "in his own flesh" is mentioned in the second register of the fifth hour. Indeed, the solar god when traveling as the "Flesh of Re" is a corpse himself, though admittedly a very powerful one capable of bringing about his own rebirth.

It is surely of interest that, upon this rebirth, Re leaves behind his mummified "Image of Flesh" leaning against the extreme boundary of the twelfth hour. Further, the corpses of the many anonymous gods residing in the regions of the Netherworld lie inert until revived for a time by the voice of Re as he talks to them. In the first register of the fifth hour the Great God himself confirms the death of gods by saying: "How beautiful is the great way inside the earth, the way to the grave and resting place of my gods," and the very name of the city of the eighth hour "Sarcophagi of her Gods" is further evidence that we have divine corpses. Presumably these gods who live in the Netherworld and who have corpses are distinguished in some fashion from the gods who live in the sky, the star-gods. Such gods are spoken to by Horus in the third register of the seventh hour, and he says to them: "May your flesh be right, may your forms come into being, so that you might be at rest in your stars." But even here a kind of resurrection from corpses is implied.

The doctrine of the secret names and forms of the gods is also briefly reflected in this book, when the gods who sit upon their hieroglyphic signs of clothing in the third register of the eighth hour are said to be like this, "as the secret forms of Horus, the heir of Osiris". In the ninth hour forms and creations or transformations (hprw) seem to lead a kind of disembodied and separate existence, for the city of the ninth cavern is named "That Which Springs Forth for Forms, That Which Lives for Transformations". Similarly the gate of the tenth hour is called "Great of Creations (or Transformations), The One Bearing of Forms." The images of the gods, presumably their statues or representations, are constantly mentioned throughout the work and obviously have special significance for the Egyptian view of the gods. While we may not know the secret forms of the gods, we can at least perceive their images, though the meaning of the images or their true nature is not knowable.

As in the case of human beings who have bas or souls that allow them after death to leave their corpses, to go forth and to return, so too the gods and deceased spirits in the Netherworld of this book have such additional spiritual personalities, and indeed the bas are included in the list of beings in the introductory table of contents whose locations in the Netherworld are to be described in the work.

## Other Works Concerning the Solar Bark

Since I have treated the cosmological aspects of the *Book of Amduat* in some detail, I can limit myself here to a briefer consideration of the other two comparable funerary books that describe the night journey of the solar bark. The work most like the *Amduat* is the *Book of Gates*.[4] Its earliest copy dates from the time of King Haremhab (1319-1307 B.C.) and is on the walls of his tomb in Thebes. It contains less than half of the work. The first complete copy is found on the sarcophagus of Seti I (1306-1290 B.C.), originally in his tomb, but now in the Museum of Sir John Soane in London. A number of its features closely resemble those of the *Amduat*: the twelve hours, the division of each hour into three registers with the middle register representing a river and the upper and lower registers its banks, the passage along the middle register by the sun bark, the form of the sun-god as a ram-headed human figure (standing in a pavilion about which the Enveloper-snake is draped) who is called The Flesh of Re. The most distinctive features of the book are the great gates at the end (according to Hornung but at the beginning according to Piankoff) of each hour, with doors guarded by snakes.

The sun-god begins the journey at the Western Desert Mountain in front of the first gate, arriving there in the beetle form, i.e. as a beetle imposed upon the sun disk and surrounded by a snake with its tail in its mouth (see Fig. II.41). This is somewhat surprising since the Khepri form of the sun-god is usually confined to its first appearance at dawn. But perhaps here it indicates that the sun begins the journey with its Khepri form gestating within the disk (fetuslike) and kept there by the surrounding snake, which, as we have seen (Chap. II, n. 27), represents the surrounding chaos out of which the sun must emerge at the end of his night journey. Also of interest to our concern with cosmogony is the fact that the crew of two that is in the bark here and throughout the night journey consists of Sia and Heka, the two gods concerned with the creative word, Heka having replaced Hu, a not uncommon substitution. Further of interest in the first hour is a brief statement over the Gods of the Western Mountain epitomizing the Great God's creation:[5]

> The ones who come into being from
> Re, from the brilliance of his eye,
> who came forth from his eye. Re
> grants them the hidden place, to
> which are brought men and gods, all
> cattle, all worms, which this Great
> God has created.

Moving to the first gate, we see a statement of Sia to the Guardian of the Desert that is of interest for the doctrine of Re's autogenesis:[6] "Open your gate to Re, You upon your door, Akhti. The Hidden Place (or Chamber) is in darkness until the creation-forms (hprw) of this god are created." After the bark with Re in his ram-headed form and his two crew members, Sia and Heka, has passed through the gate, gods come to meet the bark, and we read over them in the middle register of the second hour a statement that epitomizes the purposes of the voyage:[7]

> The sailing of this Great God on the
> ways of the Netherworld. The
> towing of this god by the gods of
> the Netherworld in order to diversify
> that which is on the earth, to take

care of those who are in it (the earth), to render judgments in the West, to make the great into the small (i.e. to equalize the differences) among the gods who are in the Netherworld, to set the spirits *(3ḥw)* in their places, to deliver the damned to their judgment, to annihilate the bodies of the wicked, to confine the bas (of whom?). Re says:.....Sia and Heka associate themselves with me in order to take care of you and to bring into being *(sḫpr)* your forms *(irw)*.

Nothing could be clearer concerning the role that Sia and Heka (Zandee has Sia, Hu, and Heka in his translation) were to have in the voyage than this statement: they were present to help the Great God create the forms of the gods, presumably by conception and magical utterance. Incidentally, in the third register, the representation of the elderly Atum leaning on his staff, which is ordinarily the evening form of Re, seems to be assisting Re, but after calling Re his father he makes it clear that they are in effect one:[8] "I am the son who comes forth from his father, and I am the father who comes forth from his son."

The gate at the end of the third hour (Fig. II.42) provides the model for the remaining gates. Like it, all contain guardians, uraei, elaborate collections of insignia or adornments *(ẖkrw)*, and erect snakes in the doorways. I note among its features that nine mummified gods are placed one upon the other in front of the gate. They are labeled as the Second Ennead and show once more the firm belief in the death of even the great gods and the application to them of the funerary practices provided for the human deceased. Similar groups of nine gods appear before the succeeding gates (the Third Ennead, the Fourth Ennead, and so on through the Ninth Ennead). One distinctive gate arrangement is found in the fifth gate (see Fig. II.43) where the Judgment Hall of Osiris is inserted between the gateway and the door, illustrating the great popularity of the imagined ceremony in which Osiris judges the dead. Not only is the Osirian judgment procedure woven into this work, but the Osirian funerary ritual as well. This is evident from the inscription that appears in the third register of the sixth hour where an address is made to mummified gods that lie on their biers, an address in which they are urged to take up their flesh, put together their bones and knit together the parts of their bodies,[9] urgings that were a part of the conventional Osirian ritual for the dead. Indeed resurrection procedures abound in this work.

In the middle register of the eleventh hour we see a cobra with one human head facing forward, another backward, and a snake's head in between (Fig. II.44). She is called "The One Who Establishes Lifespans ($^c h^c w$) and Writes them down as Years on this Uraeus".[10] I note this now only to show once more the Egyptian image of the two-headed nature of time, one head looking toward the past and the other toward the future. In the third register we see twelve goddesses with stars on their heads, who have a tow rope in their hands (see Fig. II.45). They are the hour-goddesses who guide the Great God, and Re says to them that his birth is their birth and his creation is their creation, and he tells them that they establish lifespans and give years to those who are among them.[11]

My final comments on the *Book of Gates* concern the climactic events at the end of the twelfth hour. Before the twelfth gate are two pillars with the heads of Khepri and Atum (Fig. II.46). Behind the gate we see two doors each with its guarding snake. Just beyond the doors are two figures of uraei, the one at the top of the register called Isis and the one at the bottom Nephthys. Notice that we have only one register beyond the last gate and it is devoted entirely to the rising of the sun-god in his form of the Khepri beetle. Nun, the personalized Abyss, lifts the bark (now the Daybark) up out of the abysmal waters, repeating thereby the initial creation of the Great God from the Primordial dark waters. The beetle is between the goddesses Isis and Nephthys. Above the beetle is the sun disk being received by the sky goddess Nut. She stands on the head of Osiris, "who encircles the Netherworld".[12]  The crew of the bark, which, along with Re, had only contained Sia and Heka during the night journey, now has additional gods so that the complete crew includes three unnamed gatekeepers (with door-signs over their heads), Nephthys, Khepri, Isis, Geb, Shu (*or* Maat), Heka, Hu, and Sia.[13]  The one point of interest for us is that now both Hu and Heka are together on the crew, thus intensifying the capacity of creative utterance.

The third and last book of the night voyage, which I shall discuss even more briefly than the *Book of Gates*, is the *Book of Caverns*.[14]  The earliest copy is that in the Osireion of Seti  I's temple at Abydos, built by his grandson Merneptah (1224-14 B.C.). This work differs considerably from the two works already examined. In the first place the *Book of Caverns* has only six divisions (reproduced on six tableaux). As for the registers used in these tableaux, there is no essential uniformity in the number of registers, as there was in the two other works. Actually we have only a series of somewhat disconnected scenes. As a result, there is no middle register that runs through the whole and represents the underworld river on which the solar bark moves. In fact in the six tableaux we find only one small representation of the front section of the solar bark, namely that occurring in the so-called final picture of the work (Fig. II.47), where we see the Khepri beetle rising after the front of the bark has been towed to the edge of the Abyss. In that bark we see three forms of Re, the first being a bird standing on an oval, who is Re as Osiris (it is labeled as Osiris), the second is the Khepri form, and the third is Re's night form as a human figure with a ram's head. The rising of Khepri is shown twice more in the sixth tableau.

A particularly distinctive feature of the *Book of Caverns* is the manifold use of ovals which most often are laid on their sides so that the enclosed figures of the gods simulate reclining figures. This oval is called *db't*, which is ordinarily translated as "coffin" but, as Piankoff has suggested,[15] here seems to have "the sense of an envelope or cocoon in which new life is being formed". The constant interest in revivification of the gods in this work dovetails with the paramount attention given in it to Osiris. That attention is immediately evident in the very first speech of Re in the first register of the first division:[16]

> O gods who are in the Netherworld,
> (in) the first cavern of the West,
> doorkeepers of the districts of the
> Silent Region, Ennead of the Regent

of the West (i.e. Osiris), I am Re who is in the Heaven. I enter into the utter darkness. I open the gate of the sky in the West. Behold I enter into the Land of the West. Receive me, your arms toward me. Behold, I know your place in the Netherworld. Behold, I know your names, your caverns, your secrets. I know from what you live, when the One of the Netherworld (i.e. Osiris) orders you to live. Your throats breathe when you hear the words of Osiris .... Re calls out to the gods who are in the first cavern of the Netherworld .... Behold, I enter into the beautiful West in order to take care of Osiris, to greet those who are in him. I set his enemies in their place of execution.

As Re addresses other gods he repeats that he has come to take care of Osiris. Furthermore, as we saw above, there was an identification of Re with Osiris, when he appears as a bird along with two other forms of Re in the solar bark at the end of its journey. In fact, it was not uncommon in the later period to see the mixing of Osiris and Re.[17]

### Texts and Studies of the *Book of Amduat*

The most important single work treating of the *Book of Amduat* is the edition, translation, and commentary included in E. Hornung's *Das Amduat: Die Schrift des Verborgenen Raumes (Ägyptologische*

*Abhandlungen*, Vols. 7, 13), 3 Parts (Wiesbaden, 1963, 1967). The first two parts are concerned with the longer version, Part I being the text and Part II the translation and commentary. Part III covers all aspects of the shorter version. As the result of his careful preparation of the text, Hornung's German translation is considerably more accurate than the English translation made earlier by A. Piankoff, *The Tomb of Ramesses VI*, ed. by N. Rambova (*Bollingen Series*, Vol. 40.1) (New York, 1954), pp. 227-318. A separate collection of plates appeared with this volume. Since Piankoff's work contained much which was new and ground-breaking in the study of books regarding Egyptian views of the underworld, it remains of great value to the student of Egyptian religion.

An improved German translation by Hornung, with a new metric arrangement, appeared in his invaluable *Ägyptische Unterweltsbücher* (Munich, 1972, 2nd ed. 1984), pp. 57-194.

## The English Translation

I have kept a careful eye on Hornung's German translations, but I have also followed Piankoff, who on many occasions presents an apt or picturesque rendition. We often find that the text does not contain whole sentences but only labels of what is pictured, and hence the result is a rather staccato form of expression. I have given all the pictorial representations of the hours in the form denuded of text found in Hornung's edition and in the various translations.

# Notes to the Introduction of Document II.4

1. See H. Altenmüller, "Toten-Literatur, 22. Jenseitsbücher, Jenseitsführer," *Handbuch der Orientalistik*, Abt. 1, Vol. 1, Part 2, pp. 70-72.
2. Piankoff, *The Tomb of Ramesses VI*, p. 227.
3. Altenmüller, *op. cit.* in n. 1, p. 72.
4. The text was published by C. Maystre and A. Piankoff, *Le livre des portes*, 3 vols.(Cairo, 1939-62). Volumes 2-3 were published by Piankoff alone. Piankoff also published an English translation in his *The Tomb of Ramesses VI*, pp. 137-224. Hornung was highly critical of Piankoff's text and prepared a text of his own (edited with the assistance of A. Brodbeck and E. Staehelin): *Das Buch von den Pforten des Jenseits* (*Aegyptiaca Helvetica*, Vol. 7), 2 parts (Basel and Geneva, 1979-84). The first volume contains the text and the second a German translation and commentary. See also his translation in *Ägyptische Unterweltsbücher*, pp. 54-55, 195-308. Another English version was made by J. Zandee in *Liber amicorum. Studies in Honour of Professor Dr. C. J. Bleeker* (Leiden, 1969), pp. 282-324. As I have indicated in the text, I have followed Hornung in his assumption that the gates come at the end of the hours, not at the beginning. Hence the treatment of the sun-god at the Western Mountain, which Piankoff labels as a prologue, becomes for Hornung the first hour. Hence the numbers of the hours in Hornung's version are each one number higher than in Piankoff's text and translation.
5. See Maystre-Piankoff, *Le livre des portes*, Vol. 1, pp. 15-17; Hornung, *Das Buch von den Pforten*,

Part 1, p. 1, Part 2, pp. 32-33; Hornung, *Ägyptische Unterweltsbücher*, p. 197; Piankoff, *The Tomb of Ramesses VI*, p. 141.

6. Maystre-Piankoff, *Le livre des portes*, Vol. 1, p. 25; Hornung, *Das Buch von den Pforten*, Part 1, p. 13, Part 2, p. 43; Hornung, *Ägyptische Unterweltsbücher*, p. 201; Piankoff, *The Tomb of Ramesses VI*, p. 144.

7. See the works of the preceding note: Maystre-Piankoff, pp. 30-34, 34-35; Hornung, *B.v.d.P.*, Part 1, pp. 25-30, Part 2, p. 58; Hornung, *Ä. U.*, p. 204; Piankoff, p. 146.

8. Maystre-Piankoff, Vol. 1, p. 60; Hornung, *B.v.d.P.*, Part 1, pp. 36-37, Part 2, p. 68; Hornung, *Ä.U.*, p. 206; Piankoff, p. 147.

9. Maystre-Piankoff, Vol. 2, pp. 69-70; Hornung, *B.v.d.P.*, Part 1, pp. 236-37, Part 2, p. 168; Hornung, *Ä.U.*, pp. 247-48; Piankoff, p. 176.

10. Maystre-Piankoff, Vol. 3, pp. 66-67; Hornung, *B.v.d.P.*, Part 1, pp. 365-66, Part 2, p. 257; Hornung, *Ä.U.*, p. 289; Piankoff, p. 209.

11. Maystre-Piankoff, Vol. 3, pp. 87-88; Hornung, *B.v.d.P.*, Part 1, pp. 370-71, Part 2, p. 262; Hornung, *Ä.U.*, pp. 291-92; Piankoff, p. 211.

12. Maystre-Piankoff, Vol. 3, p. 168; Hornung, *B.v.d.P.*, Part 1, p. 410, Part 2, p. 290; Piankoff, p. 224.

13. This is the order of the gods in Maystre-Piankoff, Vol. 3, p. 179, and Hornung, *B.v.d.P.*, Part 1, p. 410, Part 2, p. 290. Hornung, *Ä.U.*, p. 308, gives the following names, ordered from the bow: Sia, Hu, Heka, Maat, Geb, Isis, Nephthys, and the three Gatekeepers. Piankoff, p. 224, has a similar order except that Thoth replaces Maat.

14. A. Piankoff, *Le livre des quererts* (Cairo, 1946). Published earlier in *Bulletin de l'Institut Français*

*d'Archéologie Orientale*, Vols. 41-45 (1942-47). The latter is the version I have used. Included is the text and a French translation. Piankoff also produced an English translation in his *The Tomb of Ramesses VI*, pp. 45-133. Finally, consult the German translation of Hornung, *Ägyptische Unterweltsbücher*, pp. 311-424.

15. Piankoff, *The Tomb of Ramesses VI*, p. 47, n. 2.

16. Piankoff, *Le livre des quererts, Bulletin*, Vol. 41, pp. 7-8, plate III; Piankoff, *The Tomb of Ramesses VI*, p. 49; Hornung, *Ägyptische Unterweltsbücher*, pp. 311-12.

17. P. Derchain, *Le Papyrus Salt 825* (Brussels, 1957), pp. 35-37. See the Introduction to Doc. II.5 below.

# Document II.4

## The *Book of Amduat (Amdat)*, i. e. The *Book of What Is in the Netherworld*

### THE TITLE AND INTRODUCTION

The Writing of the Hidden Place (*or* Chamber), which [concerns] the places where the souls, the gods, the shades, and the spirits stand and what [they] do. The beginning is the Horn of the West, the Gate of the Western Horizon, the end is [The End of] Utter Darkness, the Gate of the Western (! Eastern?) Horizon. [It gives us] knowledge of the underworld souls, knowledge of what they do, knowledge of their glorifications of Re, knowledge of the mysterious souls, knowledge of what is in the hours (i.e. the regions of the hours) and their gods, knowledge of what he (Re) says to them, knowledge of the gates and the path over which the Great God passes, knowledge of the course of the hours and their gods, knowledge of those who thrive and those who are annihilated.

### TITLE OF THE FIRST HOUR

This god enters into the Western Gate of the Horizon. Seth stands on the bank of the river. There are 120 *itrw*[1] through this gateway until the bark reaches those residing in the Netherworld and passes through to Wernes.

## THE FIRST HOUR (Fig. II.29)

[*The first register, above the baboons.*] The names of the gods who open the doors for the Great Soul: Benti, Ifi, Dehdeh, The Heart of the Earth, The Sweetheart of the Earth, The One Who Praises, The One Who Opens the Earth, The Soul of the Earth, The One Whom Re Has Seen ....

[*The second register, over the first part.*] The two goddesses Truth tow this God in the Nightbark, which passes through the gateway of this city. It is 120 *itrw* (*mistakenly*, 200) after that before he reaches Wernes, which is 300 (! 309?) *itrw* in length. He grants plots of land to the gods who are in his Following. The name of this field (i.e. region) is the Water of Re. The One Who Belongs to Both Flames is the name of its guardian. This god (Re) begins to give orders and to care for those who are in the Netherworld in this field. [*Gods in the Bark of Re.*] Wepwawet (i.e. the Opener of the Ways), Sia (Understanding),[2] Lady of the Bark, The Flesh [of Re], Horus the Praiser, The Bull of Truth, The Watchful One, Hu (Authoritative Utterance), The Guider (Helmsman) of the Bark ....

[*Above the third register.*]... and this gateway, along which this god is towed in the form of a ram. He is changed after he passes this gateway, without the dead following behind him. They stand in the gateway. He gives orders to these gods whom he finds in this gateway. This is done in the secret places of the Netherworld represented like this, holy and hidden, for the few who know this.

[*Above the boat with the scarab beetle.*] Osiris, Khepri (?), Osiris .... [followed in the fourth register by the names of the baboons, twelve serpents, nine gods with lifted arms, and the names of twelve goddesses, and at the end of the division or hour there is a long passage which ends as follows:] This god passes by them (i.e. the residents at the gateway) and they wail after he has gone by them toward Wernes. It is done like this in the secret part of the Netherworld .... There are 120 *itrw* to travel to this gate. The Hour [goddess] who is the guide of this gateway is She Who Cleaves the Brows of the Enemies of Re.

## THE SECOND HOUR (Fig. II.30)
### INTRODUCTION

To rest in Wernes by the majesty of this god, to sail the fields on the Waters of Re. This field (i.e. region) is 309 *itrw* in length and 120 in width. This Great God makes grants of plots of land to the gods in this region. The name of the Night-hour [goddess] who guides this god is The Learned One, She Who Protects her Lord. The name of the gate of this city is The Devourer of All ....

This Great God makes grants of plots of land to the gods of the Netherworld. He cares for those who are in this field (region) .... These representations of the souls of the Netherworld are done in painting .... There will be offerings to them on earth in their names, which will be effective for a man on earth, as has been proved true a million times.[3] [*Above the upper register:*] They are like this. They adore this Great God after he has reached them. Their voices lead him to them. Their wailing trails him after he has given them orders [and left] .... [The gods in the first register are named.]

[*Above the solar bark in the middle register is a corrupt passage and over the bark of Re the names of the gods, where* Heka (Magic) *is substituted for* Hu.][4]

[*Above the gods of the third register we read:*]
These [gods] are like this. They present this Great God
with the year-signs.[5] They present him with
ages-branches (i.e. those representing great periods)
which they hold in their hands. This Great God gives
them orders. They call him and they live through the
voice of this Great God. Their throats breathe when he
calls them and assigns them their duties. He bestows on
them the plants which are in their fields. It is they who
give the green plants of Wernes as food to the gods
who are in the Following of Re ....

## THE THIRD HOUR (Fig. II.31)
### INTRODUCTION

[*The introduction is at the end of the second
hour:*] This Great God rests in the Field of the
Offering-dwellers and sails the Water of Osiris. This
field is 309 *itrw* in length. This Great God gives orders
to the souls who are in the Following of Osiris in this
city. The name of the Night-hour [goddess] who leads
this Great God [in this cavern] is She Who Cuts Up
Souls. The name of the gate of this city is The Seizer ....

[*Above the representations of the first register:*]
They are like this in the Netherworld in the flesh of
their own bodies. Their souls (bas) speak for them and
their shades (or shadows) rest on them .... This is what
they have to do in the West, to crush the adversary, to
cause Nun to come into being to produce the
inundation, for under them comes forth wind from the
earth ....

[*Above the second register:*] This Great God
passes along the Water of the Sole God, he who creates
food-offerings .... He travels by Osiris in this city. This
Great God rests for a time in this city and gives orders

to Osiris and to those who are in his Following ....

[*Above the third register*:] They are like this. They worship this Great God while this Great God gives them orders. They live (i.e. come alive) while he calls them .... This is what they have to do in the West: to roast and cut up the souls, to imprison the shades, to annihilate those who are the nonexistent,[6] who belong to their Place of Annihilation-houses ....

## THE FOURTH HOUR (Fig. II.32)
### INTRODUCTION

The towing of the majesty of this Great God is arrested in the mysterious Cavern of the West whose form is holy. Taking care of those who are in it without being seen by them. The name of this cavern is Life of Forms. The name of the gate of this cavern is She Who Hides the Towing. The name of the Night-hour [goddess] who leads this Great God [in this cavern] is She Whose Power Is Great. He who knows these images will eat bread beside the living in the Mansion of Atum.

The mysterious ways of Rostau, the holy roads of the Imhet Necropolis, the hidden gates in them, the Land of Sokar, He Who is on his Sand .... [Among the divinities are a number of serpents and over the one with two heads we find the name:] Neheb-kau (The Provider of Kas)[7] ....

[*Second register, above the solar bark*:] Wepwawet, Sia, Lady of the Bark, The Flesh of Re, Horus Who Praises, The Bull of Truth, The Watchful One, Hu ....

[*Third register, above the bark with the serpent*:] He is like this in his boat. He guards the Imhet Necropolis .... [*To the right of the sloping passage*:] This is the mysterious image of Imhet Necropolis. Light is on her every day at the birth of Khepri, who comes forth from the faces of the *mnmn w*-snake; then Khepri distances himself....

## THE FIFTH HOUR (Fig. II.33)
### INTRODUCTION

This Great God is towed along the right ways of the Netherworld upon the upper half of the Mysterious Cavern of Sokar, He Who Is on his Sand. Invisible and not perceptible is the image of the earth which covers the flesh of this god. The gods, among whom this god is, hear the voice of Re when he calls in the vicinity of this god. The name of the gate of this city is Stopping-point of the Gods. The name of the cavern of this god is The West.[8]  The name of the Night-hour [goddess] who guides this Great God [in this cavern] is She Who Guides within Her Bark .... The secret ways of the West, .... The Holy Place at the Land of Sokar, the Flesh, the body in (its) first manifestation-forms *(hprw)*, .... [The diagram of the road to Sokar] is made according to the plan which is drawn in the hidden region of the Netherworld ....

[*First register, above the first group of gods.*] Words said by this Great God: O Goddess of the West, give thy arm. How beautiful is the great way inside the earth, the way to the grave and resting place of my gods. May you breathe, O Ennead of gods, who came into being from my flesh when your forms *(irw)* were not yet created. May your provisions be stable. I shall protect you if you protect me. It is you whom I have decreed to be holy for protecting me in the Land of the West.

[*Second register above the solar barge.*] This

Great God travels along, being towed over this cavern in his bark [called] Life of Souls, which is in the earth. The gods of the Netherworld say to this Great God: .... Speak to Osiris, O Re. Call out, O Re, to the Land of Sokar, so that Horus on his Sand may live. Come to Khepri, O Re, Come to Re, O Khepri .... [The solar bark contains the same gods as before, once more including Sia and Hu] ....

[*Center of the third register, under the head coming out of the pyramidal mound of sand*:] The Flesh of Sokar, He Who Is on his Sand.

[*Right and left of this inscription*:] The image is like this in the thick darkness. The oval which belongs to this god (i.e. Sokar) is lighted up by the eyes in the heads of the Great God. Both legs which are inside coils of the Great God are lighted up while he protects his image ....

## THE SIXTH HOUR (Fig. II.34)
### INTRODUCTION

This Great God rests in the deep [in this cavern called] Mistress of the Inhabitants of the Netherworld. This god orders that these gods take hold of their gods-offerings in this city .... He grants them plots of land for their offerings .... The name of the gate of this city is The One with Sharp Knives. The name of the Night-hour [goddess] who guides this Great God [in this cavern] is Mesprit (Arrival), She Who Gives the Correct [Way].

[*First register*:] Words spoken by this Great God to the gods in this field :.... May you be strong in your necks (i.e., may you be very strong) and powerful in your scepters (i.e. very powerful) that you may protect Osiris against those who acted against him and who robbed him ....

[*Second register:*] This Great God travels in this
city upon the water; he rows in this field in the
neighborhood of the corpse of Osiris. This Great God
gives orders to those gods who are in the field. He
moors at those mysterious mansions which contain the
images of Osiris .... The majesty of this Great God
speaks to the Kings of Upper Egypt, who are provided
with offerings, to the Kings of Lower Egypt, and to the
Spirits who reside in this city. Your kingdoms are
yours, O Kings of Upper Egypt; may your white crowns
be consigned to you ...; your red crowns are yours, O
Kings of Lower Egypt; your spirits are yours, O Spirits
.... The Kings of Upper Egypt, who are provided with
offerings, the Kings of Lower Egypt, and the Spirits,
who are in the earth, are like this. They stand near
their caverns, and they hear the voice of this god daily
.... [Referring to the figure surrounded by the
five-headed serpent, a text says:] This is the body of
Khepri in his own flesh. The snake [called] Many Faces
guards him. He (the snake) is like this, his tail is in his
mouth[9] ....

[*Third register:*] Words spoken by this Great God
to these gods: O Gods at the head of the Netherworld,
in the Following of the Lady of the Netherworld, the
standing and sitting ones of the Abyss, who are in their
fields: You are the gods whose heads shine and whose
corpses stand. You are the goddesses who go after
Khepri to the place in the Netherworld having his
body[10] ....

THE SEVENTH HOUR (Fig. II.35)
INTRODUCTION
The majesty of this Great God rests in the

Cavern of Osiris. The majesty of this god gives orders in this cavern to the gods who are in it. This god takes another form in this cavern.[11] He turns away from Apep by means of the magic of Isis and the Elder Magician.[12] The name of the gate of this city, which this god passes by, is the Portal of Osiris. The name of this city is Mysterious Cave. The name of the Night-hour [goddess] who guides this Great God [in this cavern] is She Who Repulses the Serpent Hiu and Cuts Off the Head of the Serpent Neha-her ....

[*First register, over the gods*:] Words spoken by this Great God: O August One, give me your hand that Horus may come out of your head (*or* loins) .... This Great God speaks to Osiris, He who is in the Enveloper-snake .... [whose name is] The Enveloper, Life of Forms ....

[*Second register, over the solar bark*:] This Great God travels in this city on the road of the Cavern of Osiris, along which he is towed by the magical utterances of Isis and the Elder Magician in order to avoid the serpent Neha-her. These magical utterances of Isis and the Elder Magician are made in order to repulse Apep from Re in the West, in the hidden part of the Netherworld .... The sandbank [later named Sadjau] of Neha-her in the Netherworld is 440 cubits in its length; he fills it with his coils .... It ... is 440 cubits in width ....

[*Third register*:] This image is of Horus on his throne. This image is like this. What he has to do in the Netherworld is to set the stars into motion and to produce the positions of the hours in the Netherworld. The majesty of Horus of the Netherworld speaks to the star-gods. May your flesh be right, may your forms come into being, so that you might be at rest in your stars. May you stand up before this Re of the Horizon, who is in the Netherworld every day. You are in his Following and your stars are before him until I have wandered through the beautiful West in peace ....

## THE EIGHTH HOUR (Fig. II.36)
### INTRODUCTION

The Majesty of this Great God rests by the caverns of the mysterious, who are upon their sand [banks]. He gives them orders from his bark, and his gods tow him in this city in [his] holy form of the Enveloper. The name of the gate of this city is That Which Stands without Becoming Weary. The name of this city is Sarcophagi of Her Gods. The name of the Night-hour [goddess] who guides this Great God is Lady of the Deep Night ....

[*First register, above the first group of three divinities.*] They are like this in their dress as the secret [forms] of Horus, the heir of Osiris. This god calls to their souls after he has entered this city of the gods who reside on their sand. And there is heard from this cavern the noise of their voices like [the humming of] many bees when their souls cry out to Re. The Secret One is the name of this cavern ....

[*Second register, above the solar bark.*] This Great God travels in this city, being towed by the gods of the Netherworld, in his secret image of the Enveloper-snake .... [Above nine gods in the form of the hieroglyphic sign for Follower, i.e. in front of the eight gods who are towing the bark, we read:] It is his voice that the gods hear after he has called them while the forms of their bodies remain on their corpses which are under the sand .... When this Great God calls them, what is in them comes alive .... and what they do is to put to the sword the enemies of Re .... [Above the four rams is written:]

The Secret Images of Tatenen, the first appearances (*hprw*), the rams which are in the earth, near whom Horus has hidden the gods[13] ....

[*Third register, above the first divinities.*] They are like this, upon their clothing [signs], as the secret forms of Horus, the heir of Osiris. This Great God calls to their souls after he has entered the city of the gods who reside on their sand. This god calls out to them on both banks of the land. A cry is heard from this cavern like the caterwaul of a tomcat when their souls cry out to Re .... [and the cries of the various other divinities are compared to sundry sounds, like the roar of the living, the sound of a bank falling into the flooding water, the cry of a divine hawk, and the sound of a nest full of birds].

## THE NINTH HOUR (Fig. II.37)
### INTRODUCTION

The majesty of this Great God rests in this cavern. He gives orders from his bark to the gods who are in it (the cavern). The crew of this god rests in this city. The name of the gate of this city ... is Guardian of the Flood. The name of this city is That Which Springs Forth for Forms, That Which Lives for Transformations (*hprw*). The name of the Night-hour [goddess] who guides this Great God is She Who Adores, She Who Protects Her Lord ....

[*First register, above the twelve gods sitting on hieroglyphic signs for clothing.*] They are like this in the Netherworld, established upon their clothing-signs, in their forms and in their images made by Horus. Re speaks to them. You are provided with your clothing, you are made holy by your clothing. Horus has clothed you there just as he hid his father in the Netherworld which hides the gods ....

[*Second register.*] This Great God rests from his rowing in this city and his crew rests with his bark and his secret image of the Enveloper-snake. This Great God gives orders to the gods who are in this city. [The gods in the bark are named again, and then above the twelve gods with paddles we read:] These gods are the crew of the bark of Re, who row He Who Is In the Horizon so that he may rest in the Eastern Gate of the Sky. What they have to do is to row Re every day to this city ....

[*Third register.*] They are like this in the Netherworld, established upon their clothing-signs in their own flesh. It is they who light up the darkness in the chamber which contains Osiris. It is the flames of their mouths which overthrow enemies in the Netherworld ....

### THE TENTH HOUR (Fig. II.38)
### INTRODUCTION

This Great God rests in this cavern. He gives orders to the gods in it. The name of the gate of the city, by which the Great God enters, is Great of Creations (*hprw*), The One Bearing of Forms. The name of this city is She Who Is Deep of Water and High of Banks. The name of the Night-hour [goddess] who guides this Great God along the secret way of this city is The Raging One Who Slaughters Those Left Behind.

The Secret Cavern of the West, where Khepri rests with Re, in which gods, spirits, and the dead lament for the secret images of Igeret (the Silent Region) ....

[*First register, referring to the beetle.*] They are like this in the Netherworld in the forms and births of Khepri when he carries his egg toward this city in order to come forth afterwards in the Eastern Horizon of Heaven ....

[*Second register, above the solar bark*:] This Great God travels like this in his bark in this city. His crew of gods row him along. The gods in this city rest in the water, in which their oars are, and they breathe at the sound of the paddling of this crew of gods ....

[*Third register, referring to Horus and the drowned ones*:] Words spoken by Horus to the drowned ones, to the overturned ones, to those who float on their backs, who are in the Abyss of the Netherworld: O you drowned ones ... may there be air for your souls so that they shall not be choked, may your arms row without being hindered, may you open the right road in the Abyss with your feet, without your knees being hindered ....

## THE ELEVENTH HOUR (Fig. II.39)
### INTRODUCTION

This Great God rests in this cavern and gives orders to the gods therein. The name of the gate of this city by which this Great God enters is Restingplace of the Inhabitants of the Netherworld. The name of this city is Mouth of the Cavern, The One Who Reckons the Bodies. The name of the Night-hour [goddess], who guides this Great God [in this cavern], is Starry One, Mistress of the Bark, She Who Repulses the Rebel at His Appearance. This secret cavern of the Netherworld, which this Great God passes in order to come forth, forms the Eastern Mountain of Heaven. Everlastingness (*dt*) swallows up her images before the Seeing One,[14] who is in this city, and she gives them back [again] upon the birth of Khepri on earth ....

[*First register, referring to the first figures*:] He is

like this. He rises before Re without leaving his place in the Netherworld. He is like this. When this god calls to him, the figure of Atum appears on his back. He swallows his images afterwards. He lives on the shades of the dead, [namely] his body and his head. [The name of the first god with two heads is] The One Provided with a Face, Lord of Everlastingness.[15] [The text concerning the goddess mounted on a serpent says:] This is her own body. She is above the constellation of Shedu (?). What she has to do is to live [by means of?] the voice of Re every day. She swallows her images in this city. It is the Eleventh Hour, one of the followers of the god (i.e. Re).

[*Second register, above the solar bark:*] This Great God travels like this in this city. His crew of gods rows him toward the Eastern Horizon of Heaven. The serpent Luminous One at the bow of the boat leads this Great God toward the road of darkness, by means of which what is in it and those on earth are lighted. [The text above the twelve gods who carry the serpent reads:] They are like this before this Great God. They carry the Enveloper-snake on their heads toward this city. They pass on after Re toward the Eastern Horizon of Heaven. This god calls to them by their names and decrees for them their duties. Re says to them: May you protect your images, may you lift up your heads, may your arms be strong and your legs firm ....

[*Third register:*] Orders by the majesty of this Great God to cut to pieces those who fought his Father Osiris, the corpses of the enemies, the bodies of the dead, those who are turned upside down and are hindered from walking ....

## THE TWELFTH HOUR (Fig. II.40)
### INTRODUCTION

The majesty of this Great God rests in this cavern at The End of Utter Darkness.[16] Born will be this Great God in his forms *(ḫprw)* of Khepri at this cavern. Nun and Nunet, Heh and Hehet arise *(ḫpr)* in this cavern at the birth of this Great God that he may come forth from the Netherworld, let himself down in the Daybark, and arise from the thighs of Nut. The name of the gate of this city is That Which Praises the Gods.[17] The name of this city is Creation *(ḫpr)* from the Darkness, Appearance of Births. The name of [the goddess of] the Night-hour in which this Great God has come into being is She Who Sees the Beauty of Re ....

[*First register, above the first set of goddesses:*] They are like this in their own bodies. The uraei (cobras) come out of their shoulders after this Great God has reached this city. They are in the Following of this god. The flames of the mouths of their uraei repel the Apep-snake from Re at the Eastern Gate of the Horizon. They cross the sky in his Following in their places in the Daybark.

These gods return after this Great God has passed by the Secret Sandbank of Heaven, and they [then] rest on their thrones. It is they who gladden the hearts of the gods of the West with Re-Harakhti .... [Above the twelve adoring gods we read:] They are like this. They adore this Great God in the morning when he rests in the Eastern Gate of Heaven. They say to Re: The born is born, the created is created, the revered one of the earth, the soul of the heavenly master. The sky belongs to your soul that it may rest in it. The earth belongs to your body, O Lord of Reverence ....

[*Second register, referring to the solar bark*:] This god travels like this in this city along the backbone of this secret image of the serpent Life of the Gods when his gods tow him.[18] He enters into its tail and comes out of its mouth, being born in his forms of Khepri, and of the gods who are in his bark as well. He rests upon the secret image of Shu, who separates the sky from the earth and the complete darkness .... [Text referring to the twelve gods who tow the bark:] They are like this. They tow this Great God along the backbone of the serpent Life of the Gods .... They enter this secret image of the serpent Life of the Gods as the Honored Ones (i.e. as Elders) and they come out as the Youths of Re every day....They are in their own bodies when they come out after the Great God into the sky. The secret image of the serpent Life of the Gods is in its place in the Netherworld, and it does not any day go to any other place ....

[*Third register, referring to the group of divine couples*:] They are like this in their own bodies. They rest before Re in the sky. It is they who receive this Great God at his coming forth with them in the East of the sky every day. They themselves belong to their gate in the horizon, while their images of the Netherworld belong to this cavern .... [Above the mummy at the end of the register we read:] Image of the Flesh.[19] He is like this as an image which Horus hid in the complete darkness. It is this secret image which Shu supports under Nut, and accordingly the great flood comes forth from the earth and from this image.

# Notes to Document II.4

1. The measure of the *itrw* is about 10.5 km. It is often translated by the Latinized Greek term *schoenus* and the English word *league*. It is of interest that even in these mythologized and fanciful accounts the priestly authors attempted to give them an air of verisimilitude by inserting precise land measurements as if they were preparing regular royal itineraries.

2. There are two points of interest to us in this list of the gods accompanying the solar god. The first is that both Sia and Hu are members of his crew. Thus he has with him the two gods who are important for conceiving and uttering creative and magical words. The second is the fact that in Fig. II.39 Re has the ram-headed form which will be called "The Flesh of Re", and which will be discarded at the end of his voyage for his form of the newly created Khepri, the scarabaeus beetle.

3. This is the formula that is often added to spells, namely that they have been thoroughly tested and proved effective a million times. For example, at the end of my extract from Spell 99 of the *Book of the Dead* (Doc. II.3) we read: "A truly excellent spell (proved) a million times".

4. I have commented earlier on the virtual equivalence of Hu as personified authoritative or creative utterance and Heka as personified magical utterance. Hence it is not surprising to see Heka substituted here for Hu as a member of the crew of the solar bark. See Chapter Two, end of note 44.

5. The year-signs that these gods hold in their hands are usually identified as palm branches stripped

of their leaves and notched for counting purposes. The gods in front of them hold the longer branches, which both Piankoff and Hornung simply call measures. There seems to be little doubt, however, that they are the signs of long ages, centuries if you will, that are shown in temple reliefs as being granted to kings by the gods. The great many notches which we see on the stems of these branches are a good indication that I am correct in this assumption.

6. This is a clear reference to creatures of the chaos, those who are described as not among the beings of the cosmos. They are the truly dead, the nonexistent ones. In the very first paragraph of this work these same nonexistent beings are called the annihilated ones.

7. Neheb-kau is one of the principal creator-snakes, whose role in the early stages of creation I have mentioned in Chapter Two.

8. I follow Hornung in his interpretation of *imn* with the hill-country determinative as Amenet, i.e. the West, rather than accepting Piankoff's translation of it as the "Hidden One".

9. For comments by Hornung on the snake with the tail in his mouth, see above, Chapter Two, n. 27.

10. This is but one of many references in this work to the bodies or corpses of gods, thus illustrating how widely it was believed that gods die and their bodies are buried like those of human beings. I already spoke of this belief in Chapter Two above when I was attempting to characterize the nature of gods.

11. His form here is that of the Enveloper-snake, depicted on Fig. II.35 as the ram enveloped by a snake.

12. This illustrates that even the greatest of the gods needs the magical assistance of two such expert

practitioners as Isis and the Elder Magician. The purpose of this magic was to fend off the sun-god's perennial enemy, the snake Apep, whose harassment of Re I have mentioned above in Chapter Two. The snake is symbolic of all the difficulties and dangers to the creator god on his nightly journey of re-creation, and hence he (the snake) must be killed again and again.

13. The first part of this passage speaks of Tatenen and thus of the early stages of creation when the land rose and the first forms appeared. This no doubt reflects the popular view of Ptah as one of the great creators, and especially in his form of Ptah-Tatenen. The reference to Horus hiding the gods surely has something to do with his great struggle with Seth.

14. This is no doubt an obscure reference to the nature of eternal time and its relationship to creation. Here Everlastingness first swallows her images, which perhaps consisted of past time along with what was created, and then spits them forth anew with the rebirth of the sun and the accompanying cosmos. This might give some support to the view that eternity (nḥḥ) was the long stretch of time from the initial creation and everlastingness (ḏt) the indefinite stretch of future time.

15. Notice that the god here called the Lord of Everlastingness has two heads, one that looks behind him and the other that looks in front of him. This seems to support the comment made about everlastingness in the preceding note.

16. This is almost surely the name of the twelfth cavern. Note that it was given in the introductory paragraph at the very beginning of the work as the eastern terminus, following the name of the western

terminus.

17. The literal meaning is that this is the place that lifts up the gods, i.e. is the final place where Re and his crew are lifted up to come again into this world.

18. We have here a pictorial representation of the sun being drawn through the snake-form in order to abandon it and assume the rejuvenated form of the beetle. This is just one more reference to the important part in creation that snakes were thought to have played.

19. The discarded mummy, "Image of the Flesh", symbolizes that the sun-god has abandoned his dead, bodily form in order to be re-created as Khepri. Like all those who suffer initial death he is depicted as being mummified, thus leading to his resurrection.

# Document II.5: Introduction

## The *Litany of Re*

In my discussion of the books of the underworld voyage of the sun-god in the introduction to Document II.4, I mentioned that such books became popular additions to the tombs of the kings under the New Kingdom. Like those books, the *Litany of Re* (whose ancient title was the *Book of the Adoration of Re in the West and of the Adoration of the One Joined Together in the West*) also was concerned with the transformations of Re in the course of his daily journey as he rose every morning in a repetition of his initial creation. It is not surprising therefore that all but one of the earliest copies of this work were also found in the royal tombs (or on royal paraphernalia) in Western Thebes, in the apparent hope for the king's resurrection or re-creation like his father Re. According to Piankoff:[1]

> The main theme of the *Litany of Re* is the meeting of opposites, Re and Osiris, who become united and form an entity. This ritual is probably a part of the royal ritual to transform the Osiris-king into a new Re. The whole of the *Litany* is an amplification of a short passage of Chapter 17 of the *Book of the Dead*, describing the merging of the two opposites who become a Twin soul

[see the earlier version of this passage in Spell 335 of the *Coffin Texts* in Doc. II.2, IV, 276, 280] .... It has been suggested that the Litany is a later development of the short text (the so-called *Short Litany*) which accompanies the seventy-four figures of Re and is met with already in the tomb of Thutmosis III. These figures appear, quite apart from the *Litany*, in some later tombs--those of Seti I, Ramesses III, and others [see Figs. II.48-49] .... The seventy-four names embedded in hymnlike invocations became the first section, the beginning of the *Great Litany* .... [Certain changes brought] the total number of the divine names to 75. The oldest complete version of the *Great Litany* known to us so far is on the shroud of Thutmosis III, in the Egyptian Museum, Cairo .... The *Litany of Re* preceded by the title and the representation of the solar disk descending into the Netherworld appears first in the tomb of Seti I. It is also met with in the tombs of Ramesses II, Meneptah [or Merenptah], Amenmes, Siptah, Seti II, Ramesses III, Ramesses IV, and (in a shortened form) Ramesses IX. An abridged version ... accompanies the forms of Re in the mortuary temple of Ramesses II at Abydos. Finally, parts ... are engraved on the stone sarcophagi of the Late Period .... After a brief preface, the *Litany* opens with seventy-five invocations to the Forms of Re, followed by a series of prayers and hymns in which the identity of Re and Osiris, of whom the dead king is a manifestation, is constantly stressed .... The invocations of the seventy-five forms of Re allude to the manifestations of the divinity in the cyle of creation, his descent to the Netherworld, his death, and his rebirth. Here the thought does not develop through concepts; it is not a systematic description of a process. We are dealing with myths and allusions to them as symbols.

Since this was written E. Hornung discovered a version of the *Litany* in the tomb of Weseramon, a vizier of the time of Tuthmosis III, which seems to be the oldest known copy of the text.[2] Hornung also thoroughly disposed of the earlier view mentioned by Piankoff (in the quotation above) that a *Great Litany* grew out of a shorter *Litany* composed to go with 74 figures,[3] and he persuasively argued that the figures (76 and not the number 74 mentioned in the text) were in fact added to illustrate the manifold activities and properties of the so-called One Who Is Joined Together (i.e. Re-Osiris) during his night journey. So in fact they are not forms of Re alone that present him as an all-embracing monotheistic god of whom all other gods are merely manifestations.

In my extract below I have included only the 75 invocations to Re. We see reflected in them the main themes of creation which I have mentioned repeatedly in Chapter Two. Most of these I have called attention to in the notes to the document: the autogenesis of Re, the creation of the Ennead, Re's designation as the Weeper (i.e. the creator of man from his tears), his vivification and re-creation of the gods, souls, and spirits in the Netherworld, his granting of the breath of life, his infusion of the primordial darkness with light, his creation by authoritative word, his creation of continuous time, and so on.

## Texts and Studies of the *Litany of Re*

The first text and study of the *Litany* is that of E. Naville, *La Litanie du Soleil: Inscriptions recueillies dans les tombeaux des rois à Thèbes* (Leipzig, 1875). It includes a translation (very much out of date), a commentary, and 49 still useful plates that give transcriptions of the texts from various tombs.

The French translation of Naville's text was turned into English and published in S. Birch, ed., *Records of the Past: Being English Translations of the Assyrian and Egyptian Monuments*, Vol. 8 (London, 1876), pp. 103-28.

The first important recent work concerned with the *Litany* was that of A. Piankoff, *The Litany of Re (Bollingen Series*, Vol. 40.4) (New York, 1964). It includes a translation into English, a commentary, and plates depicting the principal copies, as well as a study of parallels to the *Litany*.

But by far the most important work to appear is the text, German translation, and commentary of E.

Hornung, *Das Buch der Anbetung des Re im Westen (Sonnenlitanei) (Aegyptiaca Helvetica*, Vol. 3), 2 parts (Geneva, 1975-76). It contains the texts of all the copies.

I have also found useful Goyon's treatment of the few fragments from the *Litany* that once appeared in Taharqa's edifice near the sacred lake at the temple of Karnak: R. A. Parker, J. Leclant, and J.-C. Goyon, *The Edifice of Taharqa by the Sacred Lake of Karnak (Brown Egyptological Studies*, VIII) (Providence, Rhode Island, and London, 1979), pp. 30-35, plates 12-15.

## The English Translation

My translation depends heavily on that of Hornung. The bold-faced numbers are those followed in Hornung's text and in the translations of Piankoff and Hornung, but at the same time they represent successive columns in most of the tomb versions. The copy in the tomb of the vizier Weseramon was abbreviated as U by Hornung. The shroud of Tuthmosis was designated as T III, the references to the other versions used by Hornung are obvious: S I and S II (tombs of Seti I and Seti II), R II, R III, R IV, and R IX (tombs of the various Ramesside kings with the designated numbers). I have generally followed the text of U and T III, as indeed did Hornung, though the other copies were also employed.

I have often added in parentheses the Egyptian words that have significance for our study of cosmogony. Some of the readings I have adopted from Hornung are clearly controversial and the reader should consult the notes to his translation for his arguments. I have occasionally used apt translations of Piankoff. I have not followed Naville and Piankoff in translating the constantly used epithet *k'-shm* as "supreme power", for it may incline readers to believe in a monotheism that is really not present in the text. Literally it means "high of power" (or more felicitously "thou with high power", as Hornung's German translation has it). I have settled for "with exalted power". Note also that I have restored the name Tatenen in the two places it appears (Invocations **3** and **66**), thus abandoning Piankoff's quite ambiguous translation "Exalted Earth". The literal meaning is, of course, "The Land Which Rises". It is the personification of a chthonic force, which, as we have seen above in Chapter Two, was joined with the name of Ptah to become Ptah-Tatenen.

# Notes to the Introduction of Document II.5

1. Piankoff, *The Litany of Re*, pp. 10-12, 16-17.
2. Hornung, *Das Buch der Anbetung des Re im Westen*, Part 1, p. vii.
3. *Ibid.*, Part 2, pp. 30-53.

# Document II.5

## The *Litany of Re*

Beginning of the Book of the Adoration of Re in the West and of the Adoration of the One Joined Together[1] in the West. This book should be recited at night after being drawn on the ground in a field.[2] This is the victory of Re over his enemies in the West. It is beneficial to a man upon earth; it is beneficial to him after he has died.

/1/ Praise to thee, Re, with exalted power, Lord of the Caverns, with hidden forms *(irw)*, he who rests in the secret [places] when he makes transformations *(ḫprw)* of himself into Deba of the One Joined Together.

/2/ Praise to thee, Re, with exalted power, this Khepri (Becoming One) who flutters his wings, who sets (descends) into the Netherworld, as he makes transformations of himself into He Who Comes Forth from His Own Members.[3]

/3/ Praise to thee, Re, with exalted power, Tatenen (*lit.* The Earth Which Rises), who fashions *(ms)* his gods, he who protects those among whom he is, he who makes transformations of himself into He at the Head of His Cavern.

/4/ Praise to thee, Re, with exalted power, who makes the earth visible, who gives light to those in the West, he whose forms *(irw)* are his becomings *(ḫprw)*, as he makes transformations of himself into his Great Disk.

/5/ Praise to thee, Re, with exalted power, with a ba

who speaks [to those in the Netherworld], he who is content with his speech, who protects the spirits (*ḥw*) of those in the West while they breathe through him.

/6/ Praise to thee, Re, with exalted power, Unique One, with powerful appearance, who is joined to his body, he who calls his gods while passing through his secret caverns.[4]

/7/ Praise to thee, Re, with exalted power, who calls his Eye, who addresses his Head, he who gives air to the bas in their places that they may receive their breaths.

/8/ Praise to thee, Re, with exalted power, he who attains his ba, who annihilates his enemies, he who decreed the punishment of the damned.

/9/ Praise to thee, Re, with exalted power, the one who is dark in his cavern, he who decrees that there be darkness in the cavern which hides those who are in it.

/10/ Praise to thee, Re, with exalted power, who gives light to the bodies, who is on the horizon, he who enters his cavern.[5]

/11/ Praise to thee, Re, with exalted power, who approaches the hidden cavern of He at the West; surely thou art the body[6] of Atum.[7]

/12/ Praise to thee, Re, with exalted power, who comes to what Anubis has interred; surely thou art the body of Khepri (the Becoming One).

/13/ Praise to thee, Re, with exalted power, whose lifetime (i.e. existence) is longer than that of the West and her images; surely thou art the body of Shu.

/14/ Praise to thee, Re, with exalted power, sparkling star for the dead; surely thou art the body of Tefnut (i.e. Tefenet).

/15/ Praise to thee, Re, with exalted power, who gives orders to the *nw*-gods (i.e. the time-gods or hour-gods) at their times; surely thou art the body of Geb.

/16/ Praise to thee, Re, with exalted power, with great examination of that place where he is; surely thou art the body of Nut.

/17/ Praise to thee, Re, with exalted power, Lord of Journeyings (? $^{jcc}w$) for those who are before him; surely thou art the body of Isis.

/18/ Praise to thee, Re, with exalted power, with shining head for that which is before him (or for those who are before him); surely thou art the body of Nephthys.

/19/ Praise to thee, Re, with exalted power, filled with members (i.e. intact in body), the Unique One, with veins joined; surely thou art the body of Horus.[8]

/20/ Praise to thee, Re, with exalted power, shaper (?), he who shines in the flood; surely thou art the body of Nun.

/21/ Praise to thee, Re, with exalted power, whom Nun protects, he who comes forth from that which he has been; surely thou art the body of the Weeper.[9]

/22/ Praise to thee, Re, with exalted power, he of the two cobras, the one ornamented (?) with two plumes; surely thou art the body of the Putrifying One (see n. 17 below).

/23/ Praise to thee, Re, with exalted power, he who enters and comes forth, and vice versa, who belongs to his secret and hidden Cavern; surely thou art the body of the *Adju*-fish.

/24/ Praise to thee, Re, with exalted power, ba to whom is presented his missing Eye; surely thou art the body of the Divine Eye.

/25/ Praise to thee, Re, with exalted power, ba who stands, Unique One, who protects what he has engendered; surely thou art the body of Netuty.[10]

/26/ Praise to thee, Re, with exalted power, with a raised head and great horns; surely thou art the Ram, Great of Forms (*or* Transformations) (*ḫprw*).[11]

/27/ Praise to thee, Re, with exalted power, he who shuts off light in the Igeret (the Silent Region); surely thou art the body of the West.

/28/ Praise to thee, Re, with exalted power, with a ba who sees in the West; surely thou art the body of the Cavern-dweller.

/29/ Praise to thee, Re, with exalted power, he of the wailing soul, the Weeper; surely thou art the body of the Mourner.

/30/ Praise to thee, Re, with exalted power, the one with the arm which comes out,[12] who is praised for his Eye; surely thou art the body of the One with Hidden Members.

/31/ Praise to thee, Re, with exalted power, the one who sinks into the Secret Region; surely thou art Khentamenti (i.e. He at the Head of the Westerners).[13]

/32/ Praise to thee, Re, with exalted power, the one rich in forms (*or* transformations) (*ḫprw*) in the Holy Chamber (i.e. the Hidden Place); surely thou art the body of the Sacred Beetle (i.e. the One Who Is Becoming) (*ḫprr*).

/33/ Praise to thee, Re, with exalted power, who gives his enemies to their guard; surely thou art the body of the One Who Is Feline (i.e. cat-headed).

/34/ Praise to thee, Re, with exalted power, who shines in the Secret Place; surely thou art the body of the Ejaculator [of semen].

/35/ Praise to thee, Re, with exalted power, with wrapped body and breathing throat; surely thou art the body of He Who Is in the Coffin.[14]

/36/ Praise to thee, Re, with exalted power, who calls

the bodies who are in the Netherworld; they breathe [accordingly] and their decay is arrested; surely thou art the body of He Who Causes [Bodies] to Breathe.

/37/ Praise to thee, Re, with exalted power, the one with mysterious face and inflamed Divine Eye; surely thou art the body of Shay (Fate).

/38/ Praise to thee, Re, with exalted power, Lord of Rising, he who alights (or comes to rest) in the Netherworld; surely thou art the body of the Ba Who Alights.

/39/ Praise to thee, Re, with exalted power, whose body is more hidden than those among whom he is; surely thou art the body of Those with Hidden Bodies.

/40/ Praise to thee, Re, with exalted power, stouter of heart than those who are in his Following, who orders heat (i.e. flames) into the Place of Annihilation; surely thou art the body of the Flaming One.

/41/ Praise to thee, Re, with exalted power, who decrees annihilation, who creates breath by means of his forms (hprw), the one who is in the Netherworld; surely thou art the body of He of the Netherworld.

/42/ Praise to thee, Re, with exalted power, thou with lifted head who presides over his time (or oval, i.e. the Netherworld), shining one in the Secret Region; surely thou art the body of the Shining One.

/43/ Praise to thee, Re, with exalted power, with joined-together members, the body of He Who Is Prominent in the Earth; surely thou art the body of He with Joined-together Members.

/44/ Praise to thee, Re, with exalted power, who creates secret things and generates bodies; surely thou art the body of the Secret One.

/45/ Praise to thee, Re, with exalted power, he who has provided for those in the Netherworld when passing the Secret Caverns; surely thou art the body of He Who Provides for the Earth.

/46/ Praise to thee, Re, with exalted power, the one whose flesh jubilates when seeing his bodies, with ba honored when passing by his members; surely thou art the body of the Jubilating One.

/47/ Praise to thee, Re, with exalted power, elevated one, with drippings from [his] Whole Eye, the ensouled one for whom his Glorious Eye is being filled; surely thou art the body of the Elevated One.

/48/ Praise to thee, Re, with exalted power, he who makes right (i.e. passable) the ways in the Netherworld and opens the roads in the Secret Region; surely thou art the body of He Who Makes Right the Ways.

/49/ Praise to thee, Re, with exalted power, the ba who travels with passing steps; surely thou art the body of the Traveler.

/50/ Praise to thee, Re, with exalted power, who gives orders to his stars when he illuminates the darkness in the Caverns, with secret forms; surely thou art the body of The Illuminating One.

/51/ Praise to thee, Re, with exalted power, who has made the caverns and who causes the bodies to come into being by what he himself has decreed;[15] mayest thou decree, O Re, for those who exist and those who do not exist,[16] for the gods, the spirits, and the dead; surely thou art the body of He Who Causes Bodies to Come into Being (shpr).

/52/ Praise to thee, Re, with exalted power, very secret one, this hidden one whose bas of the Head are like his image, who causes those in his Following to move on; surely thou art the body of the Hidden One.

/53/ Praise to thee, Re, with exalted power, with shining (or straightened) horn, Pillar of the West, with darkened locks, who is in the boiling pot; surely thou art the body of the Shining (*or* Straightened) Horn.

/54/ Praise to thee, Re, with exalted power, with exalted forms when he traverses the Netherworld and causes the bas in their Caverns to jubilate; surely thou art the body of the One with Exalted Forms.

/55/ Praise to thee, Re, with exalted power, who unites himself to the Beautiful West, at whom those of the Netherworld rejoice when seeing him; surely thou art the body of the Jubilating One.

/56/ Praise to thee, Re, with exalted power, Great Cat, who protects the gods, the judger, President of the Tribunal, he at the head of the Holy Cavern; surely thou art the body of the Great Cat.

/57/ Praise to thee, Re, with exalted power, he whose Eye rescues and whose Brilliant Eye speaks while the bodies are in mourning; surely thou art the body of He Whose Brilliant Eye Speaks.

/58/ Praise to thee, Re, with exalted power, whose ba is distant and whose bodies are hidden, he who illuminates when he sees his secret things; surely thou art the body of the Distant Soul.

/59/ Praise to thee, Re, with exalted power, with exalted ba, when he repulses his enemies, and when he decrees the flame against his transgressors; surely thou art the body of the Exalted Ba.

/60/ Praise to thee, Re, with exalted power, Putrifying One,[17] who hides the decomposition, he who has power over the bas of the gods; surely thou art the body of the Putrifying One.

/61/ Praise to thee, Re, with exalted power, the Great Elder in the Netherworld, Khepri who becomes the child (*miswritten as* the Two Children); surely thou art the body of the Child (Two Children?).

/62/ Praise to thee, Re, with exalted power, great traveler, who repeats the travels, Ba with bright body and dark face; surely thou art the body of the Dark-faced One.

/63/ Praise to thee, Re, with exalted power, who protects his body, who judges the gods as the mysterious Blazing One, who is in the Earth; surely thou art the body of the Blazing One Who Is in the Earth.

/64/ Praise to thee, Re, with exalted power, lord of bonds for his enemies, Unique One, Great One, chief of long-tailed monkeys; surely thou art the body of the One Who Binds.

/65/ Praise to thee, Re, with exalted power, who orders fire into his cauldrons, who severs the heads of the annihilated ones; surely thou art the body of He of the Cauldron.

/66/ Praise to thee, Re, with exalted power, generator with completed forms (or fashionings), Unique One, who lifts up the earth by his magical power; surely thou art the body of Tatenen (The Earth Which Rises).

/67/ Praise to thee, Re, with exalted power, for whom the awakened ones rise,[18] [for] those who are on their biers without seeing their secrets; surely thou art the body of the Awakened Ones.

/68/ Praise to thee, Re, with exalted power, Djenty[19] of the sky, star of the Netherworld, who causes [his] mummies to come forth (or whose mummies flow forth); surely thou art the body of the One Who Causes Bodies to Come Forth.

/69/ Praise to thee, Re, with exalted power, the cheering baboon, thou of Wetjenet (i.e. the desert homeland of the sun in the east), Khepri, thou with just forms; surely thou art the Baboon of the Netherworld.

/69/ Praise to thee, Re, with exalted power, the cheering baboon, thou of Wetjenet (i.e. the desert homeland of the sun in the east), Khepri, thou with just forms; surely thou art the Baboon of the Netherworld.

/70/ Praise to thee, Re, with exalted power, he who renews the earth and opens up what is therein, thou with the ba who speaks and extols his members;[20] surely thou art the body of He Who Renews the Earth.

/71/ Praise to thee, Re, with exalted power, Nehi,[21] who burns his enemies, flaming one, with fire-spitting tongue; surely thou art the body of Nehi.

/72/ Praise to thee, Re, with exalted power, traveler with passing glance, one who causes darkness to come into being after his light [passes]; surely thou art the body of the Traveler.

/73/ Praise to thee, Re, with exalted power, Lord of Bas, he who is in his Benben-house,[22] chief of the gods who are in the Forehall; surely thou art the body of the Lord of Bas.

/74/ Praise to thee, Re, with exalted power, glittering light (?), he of the Benben-house, who ties time together;[23] surely thou art the body of the Glittering Light (?).

/75/ Praise to thee, Re, with exalted power, Lord of Darkness, who speaks as a corpse, ba who calls to those who are in the Caverns; surely thou art the body of the Lord of Darkness.

*{For the notes to this document, see page 527.}*

# Notes to Document II.5

1. Piankoff, *The Litany of Re*, p. 11: "In the *Litany* we meet two terms: 'The One Joined Together' and 'Deba of the Joined Together'. On the representations of the forms of Re [see Fig. II.49. Reg. 1], this last name accompanies a figure of a mummiform Osiris wearing the crown of Upper Egypt. It obviously depicts Osiris infused with the soul of Re." See also Fig. II.50.

2. *Ibid.*, p. 22, n. 3: "The 75 forms of Re were drawn on the ground and the text was pronounced over them."

3. This expresses Re's autogenesis as mirrored by his daily rising in the form of Khepri.

4. We recall that in the *Book of Amduat* the Great God called to the inert gods of the various caverns and revivified them, at least temporarily, with his voice.

5. Piankoff, *The Litany of Re*, p. 23, n. 16: "The first ten Invocations apply to Re in his two aspects, the solar and the Osirian. In the tomb of Mentuemhat these forms are disposed in such a way that the solar forms are above, the Osirian below. Invocations 1,3,5,7,and 9 are addressed to the Osirian forms (Pl. 2)."

6. *Ibid.*, n. 17: "*Body* or *bodies* are used without discrimination. T III has 'bodies' in Invocation 11, 'body' in Invocations 12-17, 19, then 'body' seems to prevail." But I follow Hornung and use "body" everywhere.

7. After mentioning the bodies of Atum and Khepri (the before and the after forms of the Great God during the night journey), the author gives invocations to Re's manifestations as various Gods of the Ennead:

Shu, Tefenet, Geb, Nut, Isis, Nephthys. He then jumps to Horus, omitting Osiris and Seth.

8. Piankoff, *The Litany of Re*, p. 24, n. 26: "All energy is being concentrated for the birth of the new sun in a new cycle. Invocations 11 to 19 represent the act of creation."

9. The reference is probably to Re as the creator of man, since man was created from the tears of Re, as I often remarked in Chapter Two above.

10. For Netuty, see E. Hornung, *Das Buch der Anbetung des Re im Westen*, Part 2, p. 107, n. 73.

11. Piankoff, *The Litany of Re*, p. 24, n. 34: "Re goes down into the Netherworld 'in the form of a ram' .... The ram with the attached head is a symbol indicating that the dying god is going to rise again."

12. We recall that the Disk (Aten) in the Amarna representations has arms coming out of it (see Fig. II.23).

13. The identification here is with Osiris, not with the older god whose epithet Osiris absorbed.

14. Piankoff, *The Litany of Re*, p. 25, n. 39. In the text Piankoff gives his name as Debaty and in the note presents "He of the Coffin" and "He who adorns" as alternative translations.

15. This is surely a reference to creation by the authoritative word.

16. I have remarked on the significance of this phrase for the Egyptian doctrines of creation, the existent things being those of the cosmos, the nonexistent being those of chaos.

17. See Hornung, *Das Buch der Anbetung des Re*, Part 2, p. 116, n. 167.

18. Piankoff. *The Litany of Re*, p. 28, n. 63: "In the *Pyr. Texts* the dead king is received by Geb, who

places him at the head of the spirits, the Imperishable Stars, then: 'They of the secret place adore thee; the great assemble for thee; the watchers stand before thee' (Sect. 656de). The watchers are the gods sitting behind Amon: *Wörterbuch-Belegstellen*, I, 40."

19. See Piankoff, *The Litany of Re*, p. 28, n. 64, for a discussion of the *djent*-jar, which "is the cradle and at the same time a vessel for crossing the celestial waters [*Pyr. Texts*] Sect. 1185;...".

20. Piankoff, *The Litany of Re*, p. 28, has "rearer of his members". The reading I have adopted for *rnn* is in accord with the determinative. Goyon, *The Edifice of Taharqa*, p. 35, translates the phrase by "naming his members". See also n. 55 on that page for a further name added to this invocation.

21. See Hornung, *Das Buch der Anbetung des Re*, Part 2, p. 120, n. 194.

22. This is the name of the temple at Heliopolis housing the pyramidal Benben-stone.

23. Piankoff, *The Litany of Re*, p. 28, n. 70, interpreting this phrase, says: "i.e., makes time continuous". In line with what I have already said about Egyptian conceptions of time, this probably means he put together "eternity" and "everlastingness" or past and future time to produce eternal time.

# Document II.6: Introduction

## The *Book of the Divine Cow*

I have mentioned on more than one occasion in Chapter Two the work that is known to modern readers as the *Book of the Divine Cow* (or often, the *Book of the Celestial Cow*). It has considerable interest for the student of ancient Egyptian cosmogony. The first part of this text (columns 1-35) has been known in modern times as the *Destruction of Man* since the subject of that part is man's plotting against the aging Re and the consequences of that act. Of that first part I shall include only the beginning in Document II.6 below.

As with Documents II.4 and II.5, its earliest extant copies appear in the royal tombs of the New Kingdom: those of Tutankhamen (only fragments), Seti I, Ramesses II, Ramesses III, and Ramesses VI. Its opening sentence contains a standard reference to Re as "the god who created himself". But as I said earlier and point out in the notes below, a later assertion of Nun speaks of Re as being greater than the god that made him (by which Nun apparently means himself) and older than the gods that created him (the Ogdoad in the Abyss?). If indeed these gods that created him are the Ogdoad of the Abyss, it is probably they whom Re addresses along with Nun when he mentions the plot of mankind against him. Whoever they are, he calls them the primeval or ancestor gods. It may also be these same gods that were intended when Re called to his side "the fathers and mothers who were with me when I was in the Abyss" along with his Eye, the first generations of the Ennead after him (Shu and Tefenet, Geb and Nut), as well as Nun. Hence it is obvious that the text does not confine itself to the simple Heliopolitan doctrine of autogenesis.

It is also clear that the *Book of the Divine Cow* introduces a distinct variation in the Heliopolitan plan, for it describes in the beginning an earlier time in the evolution of creation when Re ruled the gods and men together on the earth, a time when no heaven existed, no support gods, and no stars. At this simple stage of creation a complication was introduced by the fact that Re had aged and his human subjects began to plot against him. The result told here is that mankind was partially extinguished by Re's Eye in the form of Hathor, and, though Re spared the rest of mankind, he made firm his decision to leave the earth, to return to the Abyss, or at least to a place in the sky. The consequences of that decision are briefly given here: the transformation of Nut into the sky (in the form of the celestial cow on whose back Re himself had climbed in order to be removed from the earth), the assignment to Shu of the task of lifting and holding Nut up with the help of newly created Heh-gods (support gods), and the creation of the stars for gods and deceased spirits and their location in the sky.

Further, we are told that Geb was to look out for the snakes in the earth and their magic. Geb was to have the help of Thoth's skill in writing. But we see that Thoth himself was to be not only Re's scribe but his vicar in the Netherworld, Re having removed himself from the earth and the underworld and being content to be located in the sky. The preoccupation with snakes, those early cosmogonic figures, is of interest. It is not by accident that so much of the last part of the work is concerned with magical spells that would be effective protection against the enemies of Re. It is accordingly of great interest that in the last section we find, in the so-called "theology of the bas", that Re's ba is Magic. I note also that the bas listed for the gods seem to be the personifications of their most important powers or attributes, sometimes in the form of another god (see note 26 of Document II.6).

Hornung draws the conclusion that man's rebellion and Re's departure from earth meant a rupture of the initial union of man and gods, a union to be replaced by their hoped-for, future association as celestial beings or spirits, an association by no means elaborated on in this work.[1] In this intriguing leap Hornung sees the main features of the Egyptian cosmogonic and funerary doctrines accepted in the New Kingdom. He regards as an important aspect of the new form of creation described in this work the attention given to the supporting of the sky, and indeed not only does Shu play an important role in the support of Nut, along with the support given by the newly created Heh-gods, but the Pharaoh too is conceived as having a role similar to that of Shu (see Fig. II.51), being like Shu a son of Re.

Furthermore, Eternity and Everlastingness, those two components of eternal time, are personified, and, as seen in Fig. II.52, play their role in supporting the sky. The importance of the creation of the sky and its support is shown by the centrality of the celestial cow herself. The description of the picture (Fig. II.2a) appears at the center of the work and in itself embraces the main results of the celestial creation: the sky as the belly of the cow, the stars of an extended Ennead on the belly, the solar bark moving across the belly, the depicted Heh-gods, the "Millions" (of stars), all consequences of Re's decision to retreat from his earthly rule. On the whole, Hornung gives more coherence than earlier students to the ideas found in the *Book of the Divine Cow*.

Texts and Studies of the *Book of the Divine Cow*

The earlier texts and studies are conveniently listed in E. Hornung, *Der ägyptische Mythos von der Himmelskuh: Ein Ätiologie des Unvollkommenen* (Göttingen, 1982), p. xi. Hornung's work displaces most of the earlier studies. It not only contains the versions of all the copies, but it also provides a new and very revealing translation, with perceptive notes and an overall discussion of the work.

We should mention that the first edition of all the versions is found in C. Maystre, *Le livre de la vache du ciel dans les tombeaux de la Valle des Rois (Bulletin de l'Institut Français d'Archéologie Orientale*, Vol. 40) (Cairo, 1940).

Note also the complete German translation in G. Roeder, *Urkunden zur Religion des alten Ägypten* (Jena, 1923), pp. 142-49, and the complete English translation of A. Piankoff, *The Shrines of Tut-ankh-Amon (Bollingen Series*, Vol. 40.2) (New York, 1955), pp. 17-34.

There are several partial texts and translations listed by Hornung. One of the most important of these is the translation of E. Brunner-Traut, *Altägyptische Märchen* (Düsseldorf and Cologne, 1963), pp. 69-72, 266-67.

### The English Translation

My translation is heavily dependent on the German translation of Hornung. The reader is advised to examine Hornung's notes in which he attempts to justify his many departures from the more common interpretations. Most of these departures are convincing, but in a few cases I have seen fit to substitute my own renderings. The numbers employed in the translation are (approximately) the column numbers of the version in Seti I's tomb.

# Note to the Introduction of Document II.6

1. Hornung, *Der ägyptische Mythos*, pp. 74-105, discusses all aspects of the work.

# Document II.6

## The *Book of the Divine Cow*

/1/ It happened that Re arose [or shone], the god
who created himself, after he took over the kingship,
when men and gods were [still] united [on earth]. Then
men devised /2/ plots against Re, for his majesty,
L.P.H., had grown old, and his bones became like silver,
his flesh like gold, his hair like real lapis lazuli.[1] His
majesty had learned /3/ about the plots that were being
devised by men against him. Then his majesty, L.P.H.,
said to those [gods] who were in his Following: "Call to
me my Eye,[2] Shu, /4/ Tefenet, Geb and Nut, together
with the fathers and the mothers who were with me
when I was in the Abyss (the four pairs of the
Ogdoad?), as well as Nun (the god of the Abyss). Let
him (Nun) bring his attendants /5/ with him. Bring
them secretly so that men will not see [them] and their
hearts will not flee.[3]   Come with them to the palace
and let them tell their private plans /6/ so that I may
go [back] into the Abyss to the place in which I came
into being."[4]

These gods were brought and they were lined up
on both sides of him with their heads bent to the earth
/7/ before his majesty, that he might speak his words
before the father of the eldest ones (*or* before the
eldest father), the maker of men, the king of people
*(rhyt)*. Then they said to his majesty: "Speak /8/ to us
that we might hear." Then Re said to Nun: "O Eldest

God in whom I came into being[5] and you primeval gods, behold, men, who came into being /9/ from my Eye,[6] devise plots against me. Tell me what you would do about it. Behold, I do not seek to kill them before having heard what you will say /10/ on the matter."

Then spoke the majesty of Nun: "My son Re, a god greater than he who made him and older than those who created him,[7] stay on thy throne, /11/ for great is the fear of thee when thine Eye is on those who scheme against thee"[8] ..... [They advise him to send his Eye out against rebellious mankind, and he does so, she taking the form of Hathor. She slays many men the first day and reports back to Re, who relents and decides to thwart a second day of slaughter. This is accomplished by the mixing of red ochre with beer and spreading it "3 palms (deep)" over the place where the destruction is to take place. Then when the goddess shows up the next morning, she drinks the beer, becomes drunk, and does not recognize man. The latter is thus spared. The other worthwhile consequence of Re's action, we are told, is the custom of the preparation of intoxicating drinks by servant girls on the Feast of Hathor!]

[In the second part of the work, Re decides to withdraw from his earthly rule and go back to the Abyss, assigning other gods their places and creating still others by authoritative commands.]

/27/.... Then the majesty of Re said: "As truly as I live, my heart is very weary of being with them (mankind). I shall kill them, without exception, and the /28/ reach of my hand (i.e. power) will not be narrow."[9]  The gods who were in his Following said: "Do not escape into your weariness, for thou hast power over the things thou likest (or what thou wishest)." Then said the majesty /29/ of this god to the majesty of Nun: "My limbs are (or body is) weak as in (or for) the first time. I will not return so that another will attack me."

Then the majesty of Nun said: "My son Shu, [keep] thine eye /30/ upon [thy] father as his protection. My daughter Nut, put him [on thy back]." Then said Nut: "What meanest thou, my father Nun?" Then Nut said [further]: /31/ "In ... Nun." Nut transformed herself [into a cow] and the majesty of Re [climbed] on her back. These men /32/ [returned from the place to which they had withdrawn] and then they saw him on the back of the cow.[10] Then these men spoke /33/ to him: ".... [Come?] to us, for we shall overthrow thine enemies, who have devised plots against him who created them." [But] his majesty proceeded /34/ to [his] palace [on the back of] this cow. [Nothing?] came with them. And so the land was in darkness. When the land had become light [again] at dawn, these men /35/ came out carrying their bows[11] .... [A battle ensues, from which, the Great God remarks, human battles ("massacre among men") arose. Then follows a series of creations by authoritative command.]

/36/ .... Then this god spoke to Nut: "I have set myself upon thy (*miswritten* my) back in order to lift myself up." /37/ "What does this mean?" asked Nut. And she became [thereupon] the Dweller in Both Skies. The majesty of this god said: "Be far from them and near to me in order to see /38/ me." So she was transformed into the sky. Then the majesty of this god looked inside her and she said: "Would that I were provided with /39/ a multitude of beings." Thereupon the ... [the stars or some epithet of Nut?][12] came into being. Then said his majesty, L.P.H.: "Peaceful (*ḥtp*) is the field here." Thereupon came into being the Field of Offering

(*Htp*).[13]  "I will cause green plants to grow /40/ in it"--and thus came into being the Field of Rushes.[14]  "I will provide it (the sky) with all kinds of things," which are the *ihihw*-stars (i.e. the ever-shining stars).[15]  Then Nut /41/ began to shake because of the height, and then the majesty of Re spoke: "Would that I had *hh*-gods to support her"; and thus the Heh-gods were caused to come into being.[16]  Thereupon the majesty of Re spoke: /42/ "My son Shu, place thyself under my daughter Nut, and the Heh-gods shall guard for me the Millions [of bas] there,[17] that they might live [again] in the twilight.  Take /43/ her upon thy head to stabilize her." And [so] it came about that a nursemaid is given to a son or daughter and it came about that a son is placed by a father on his /44/ head.

This spell is to be spoken over [a picture of] a cow [see Fig. II.2a][18] .... /56/ Then the majesty of this god said to Thoth:[19] "Pray call to me the majesty of Geb in these words: 'Come immediately.'" And the majesty of Geb came there. Thereupon spoke the majesty of this god: "Watch out /57/ for thy snakes which are in thee (i.e. in the earth). Behold I am afraid of them myself when I am there. But thou knowest their [magical] power. Go then to the place in which my father Nun is and say to him: 'Watch out /58/ for snakes which are in the land and the water and for every place in which thy snakes are put in writing the following: *Guard against playing with anything*'. They know that I am here. /59/ Behold I rise for them [also], and as for their need it will be [given to them] in the land forever. Beware also of those magicians /60/ who know their spells, for the god Heka (Magic) is there himself .... I do not myself need to guard the great god who came into being /61/ before me, for I have assigned them (the snakes) to Osiris, who guards their children, and I have caused the hearts of their elders to forget. Give their [spiritual] power, which has been made according to /62/ their desires, to the whole land as their magical words which are in their bodies."

Thereupon spoke the majesty of this god: "Now call Thoth to me." And he was brought immediately. Then spoke the majesty /63/ of this god to Thoth: "Behold, I am here in the sky /64/ in my place. Since I /65/ shall produce light and brilliance /66/ in the Netherworld and in the Island of the Double Soul,[20] /67/ thou shalt write there and thou shalt make impotent those who are in /68/ them which we created and who [later] produced /69/ rebellions .... /71/ Thou shalt be in my place, my representative. Men shall address thee as 'Thoth the Representative of Re', and I shall cause thee to send out [emissaries] who are greater than thou." So came into being the ibis of Thoth.[21] "I shall /72/ cause thy hand to be stretched out in the presence of the primeval gods, who are greater than thou, and it will be good for me when thou dost [it]." So came into being the ibis-bird of Thoth.[22] "I shall cause thee to /73/ encompass both skies with thy beauty and with thy light." So came into being the moon of Thoth.[23] "I shall cause thee to turn back the Haunebu." So came into being the baboon of Thoth.[24] ... [Then follows a description of spells and their magical effects, the last of which is effective "a million times".]

/84/ .... Nun was embraced by the Eldest God himself (i.e. Re), who said to the gods who came forth from the East of the Sky [with him]: "Give praise to the [truly] Eldest God (i.e. Nun), [for] I have come into being /85/ from him. I have made the sky and stabilized [it] in order that the bas of the gods might be set in it. I am with them an eternity *(nḥḥ)*, which the years have formed *(ms)*.[25] Magic (Heka) is my ba and accordingly it (Magic?) is older than it (i.e. the eternity?)."

The ba of Shu is Khnum (*var.* the air).[26] /86/ The ba of Eternity is the rain. The ba of Darkness is the night. The ba of Nun is Re (*var.* water). The ba of Osiris is the Ram of Mendes. The bas of Sobek are the crocodiles. The ba /87/ of every god and every goddess is in the snakes. The ba of Apep is in the Eastern Mountain, while the ba of Re is throughout the whole earth (*var.* is in Magic) .... [The remainder of the work continues with magical spells, of which I note only that one spell contains the following:] /89/ I am his (Re's) ba, Heka. O Lord of Eternity *(nḥḥ)*, who has created Everlastingness *(dt)*, who causes the years of the gods to pass (*lit.* to be swallowed up), and in whom Re has descended, lord of his own god[liness] and ruler of him who has created him ....

# Notes to Document II.6

1.   This appears to be an almost conventional way of referring to the aged Re, as I noted above in Chapter Two (see also Document II.11, H,3-4). The god is being depicted in terms applicable to a statue made of precious metals and stones.

2.   The Eye of Re had long since assumed its separate existence as a divinity, and when taking the form of the Uraeus on his forehead she was the Great God's protector, as she was later the protector of his son, the king.

3.   For an explanation of this expression, see Hornung, *Der ägyptische Mythos*, p. 53, n. 14, referring to its use in medicine for a fainting spell. But this still does not make clear what it means in this context. What reaction in man was secrecy supposed to forestall?

4.   Here he declares the conventional Heliopolitan view of Re's coming into being in the Abyss.

5.   The Abyss has become personified as the father of Re, but a father inferior to his son.

6.   Here we have a reference to the view that mankind arose in the tears of the creator.

7.   The creation of Re is even more confused in this passage since the first reference is apparently to his creation by Nun, only to be followed by an allusion to "those who created him". It could perhaps reflect the doctrine of the Ogdoad, which, as we have seen, presents the negative characteristics of the Abyss as four pairs of divinities.

8.   See Hornung, *Der ägyptische Mythos*, p. 54, n.

30.

9. *Ibid.*, p. 59, n. 75.

10. For the reconstruction of this sentence, see *ibid.*, nn. 82-85.

11. This obscure account of a war between factions of mankind (those for Re and those against him) is given as the origin of human massacres. The passage is however not at all clear, at least so far as the identification of the contestants is concerned.

12. For these two alternative interpretations, see Hornung, *Der ägyptische Mythos*, p. 61, n. 102. I lean toward the second of the alternatives, for the actual creation of the stars is mentioned later.

13. Here begins the series of word-plays by which creation of different places and divinities takes place. For this example I have given the Egyptian words expressing this word-play in parentheses. In the succeeding examples I have cited the relevant notes of Hornung.

14. These two celestial fields, which I have discussed in Chapter Two above, have been successively created. The punning involved in the second case, that is, in this sentence, is quite contrived. See Hornung, *Der ägyptische Mythos*, p. 61, n. 105.

15. These stars are usually called *ꜥhꜥhw*-stars rather than *iḫiḫw*-stars. For the punning involved, see Hornung, *ibid.*, n. 106.

16. We have already mentioned the Heh-gods, which appeared so often in the *Coffin Texts*. They are shown supporting the legs of the celestial cow in Fig. II.2a.

17. The same hieroglyph is used for the Heh-gods and for the Millions [of stars]. Hence once more word play is crucial to the creation. These

Millions are, of course, the bas of the gods and the deceased that populate the sky.

18.    There follows in the text a detailed description of the picture of the celestial cow. For a comparison between the description and the surviving pictures, see Hornung, *ibid.*, pp. 62-64, nn. 113-35; pp. 81-85.

19.    It is evident that here Thoth is performing his secretarial duties as the Scribe of Re. After Geb has been called, he is charged with guarding against the snakes that are in the earth and the water. Nun in the Abyss is also to be brought into the control of the snakes, presumably those in the waters that constitute the Chaos. Osiris was to have control over the snakes in the Underworld. All of the commands issued by Re in regard to the snakes are a part of his divesting himself of control in the lower regions since he has removed himself therefrom into the sky.

20.    Here Re declares that he is in his place in the sky, but, since he will give light to the Netherworld and to the so-called Island of the Double Soul (i.e. the United One, consisting of Osiris and Re?), he commands that Thoth will become his representative in those regions, and Thoth is to exercise the power of his pen to "write there" and render impotent those whom Re created (i.e. men) and who later rebelled against him.

21.    The play on words for the creation process here is the similarity between "send out" *(h'b)* and "ibis" *(hby)*.

22.    For the word play, see Hornung, *Der ägyptische Mythos*, p. 67, n. 164.

23.    For the word play, again see Hornung, *ibid.*, n. 166.

24.    *Ibid.*, n. 168.

25. My translation differs from that of Hornung. My emphasis is that the years [of the past] have already formed an eternity *(nḥḥ)*. Hence Re's ba, which is Magic, must share the timelessness of Re and therefore be older than the Eternity which the years since the first creation have brought into being.

26. This excursus on bas is of considerable interest. The bas all seem to involve word play, while revealing important attributes of the gods named. See the various notes to this passage given by Hornung, *ibid.*, pp. 69-70, nn. 191-96.

# Document II.7: Introduction

## Hymns

All but the first of the various hymns I have presented here as Document II.7 touch rather directly on the subject of Chapter Two, cosmogony and cosmology. The first, the Great Hymn to Osiris, has been included because it contains the most extensive references to the Osiris legend in Egyptian sources. It does however in its second stanza emphasize the power that Osiris possessed in the already created world, as I have pointed out in Chapter Two above.

The cosmogonic doctrines found in the remaining hymns (those to Amon-Re in Documents II.7b[1-4], to Aten in II.7c, to Ptah in II.7d, and to Khnum and Neith in II.7e) have been summarized in Chapter Two and this summary should serve as an adequate introduction to this collection of hymns celebrating and describing the creation as assigned to each of these gods. Before presenting the documents themselves I give the usual bibliographical references to texts and translations. In doing so I depart from the usual style by including the remarks on my English translations within these bibliographic sections. I further note that the translations of II.7a and II.7c are those done by Miriam Lichtheim, while all the others are my own (in which I have made free use of renderings from previous translations where they seem to me to be felicitous).

# ANCIENT EGYPTIAN SCIENCE

## Texts and Studies of the Hymns

(*Doc. II.7a*). The text of the stela (Louvre C 86) on which the Great Hymn to Osiris is inscribed was published by A. Moret, "La légende d'Osiris à l'époque thébaine d'après l'hymne à Osiris du Louvre," *Bulletin de l'Institut Français d'Archéologie Orientale* Vol. 30 (1931), pp. 725-50, and plates I-III. It was republished by A. de Buck, *Egyptian Reading Book*, Vol. 1 (Leiden, 1948), pp. 110-13. A German translation was given by G. Roeder, *Urkunden zur Religion des alten Ägypten* (Jena, 1923), pp. 22-26, and more recently by J. Assmann, *Ägyptische Hymnen und Gebete* (Zurich and Munich, 1975), pp. 443-48, 625-26. An English version appeared in the English translation by A. M. Blackman of A. Erman, *The Literature of the Ancient Egyptians* (London, 1927), pp. 140-45 (later reprinted as *The Ancient Egyptians. A Sourcebook of their Writings*, with an introduction by W. K. Simpson [Harper Torchbook, New York, 1966]). The best translation seems to me to be that of M. Lichtheim, *Ancient Egyptian Literature. A Book of Readings*, Vol. 2 (Berkeley/Los Angeles/London, 1976), pp. 81-86, and indeed I have given that translation here, adding the line numbers from the Moret text. I have occasionally given Egyptian words and topographical identifications within parentheses.

(*Doc. II.7b[1]*) The initial publication of the text of this hymn to Amon-Re (or Min-Amon) from Papyrus Boulaq 17 in the Cairo Museum was done by A. Mariette, *Les papyrus égyptiens du Musée de Boulaq*, Vol. 2 (Paris, 1872), p. 6 and plates 11-13. This papyrus was from the eighteenth dynasty. It was studied and edited by E. Grébaut, *Hymne à Ammon-Ra* (Paris, 1874), who also gives a French translation. This hymn also appeared in incomplete fashion on statue no. 40950 of the British Museum, dating from the Middle Kingdom, as noted and studied by S. Hassan, *Hymnes religieux du moyen empire* (Cairo, 1928), pp. 157-93. Hassan gives the text of the parts on the statue alongside the text given by Grébaut (with French translation), and he adds a running commentary. Parts of the text have been translated often: Roeder, *Urkunden*, pp. 4-8; Erman, *The Literature*, pp. 282-88; John Wilson, in J. Pritchard, ed., *Ancient Near Eastern Texts Relating to the Old Testament* (Princeton, 1950, 2nd ed., 1955), pp. 365-67; Assmann, *Ägyptische Hymnen*, pp. 199-207. I have employed Assman's divsions A-G in my translation, with the column and line numbers of the papyrus in parentheses.

(*Doc. II.7b[2].*) This hymn appears in two stelas from the Theban tomb of the Overseers of the Works of Amun under Amenhotep III: Seth and Horus. The stelas are no. 34051 of the Museum at Cairo and no. 826 of the British Museum. The stela from the Cairo Museum is in wretched condition; therefore my translation is made from that in the British Museum and I employ its line numbers in my translation. For the text, see I.E.S. Edwards, *British Museum, Hieroglyphic Texts from Egyptian Stelae*, Part VIII (1939), pp. 22-25, plate XXI; A. de Buck, *Egyptian Reading Book*, pp. 113-15; A. Vareille, "L'hymne au soleil des architectes d'Amenophis III Souti et Hor," *BIFAO*, Vol. 41 (1942), pp. 25-30 (with two plates), including a French translation; and W. Helck, *Urkunden der 18. Dynastie* (=*Urkunden* IV), Heft 21 (Berlin, 1958), pp. 1943-46. There are many translations, the earlier ones being listed in the article by Vareille. Of the more recent ones I found the English translation by Wilson in Pritchard, *Ancient Near Eastern Texts*, pp. 367-68, and the German translation of Assmann, *Ägyptische Hymnen*, pp. 209-12, 555-57, the most useful.

(*Doc. II.7b[3].*) The initial text and English translation were made by A. H. Gardiner, "Hymns to Amon from a Leiden Papyrus," *ZÄS*, Vol. 42 (1905), pp. 12-42. See also the text of J. Zandee in his study of this papyrus: *Hymnen aan Amon van Papyrus Leiden I 350* (Leiden, 1948), Bijlage 1, Hieroglyphische Tekst, plates I-VI. Wilson gives extracts in Pritchard, ed., *Ancient Near Eastern Texts*, pp. 368-69. Consult the extracts in German translation by Assmann, *Ägyptische Hymnen*, pp. 312-21, 586-89. My translation owes much to Gardiner's. Note that the chapter numbers were artificially selected for the purpose of punning and do not represent truly successive ordinals, the first nine chapters being numbered by units, the next nine by tens, and the final eight by hundreds.

(*Doc. II.7b[4].*) I have used the text published by W. Golénisheff, ed., *Papyrus hiératiques (Catalogue général des antiquités du Musée du Caire*, Vol. 83, Nos. 58001-58036) (Cairo, 1927), pp. 171-77. The bracketed numbers given in my translation are the line numbers given by Golénisheff. See also the German translation of E. Meyer, "Gottesstaat, Militärherrschaft und Ständewesen in Ägypten," *Sitzungsberichte der Preussischen Akademie der Wissenschaften, Jahrgang 1928, Phil.-hist. Klasse* (Berlin, 1928), pp. 503-08 (whole study, pp. 495-532). It was later translated into English by A. Piankoff, *Mythological Papyri, Edited with a*

*Chapter on the Symbolism of the Papyri by N. Rambova, (Bollingen Series,* Vol. 40.3) (New York, 1957), pp. 13-14. Piankoff failed to translate the text after "heart" in line 39. The most accurate of the modern translations is that in German by Assmann, *Ägyptische Hymnen und Gebete,* pp. 308-12, 584-85.

(*Doc. II.7c.*) For the text of the Great Hymn to the Aten, see N. de G. Davies, *The Rock Tombs of El Amarna,* Part 6 (London, 1908), pp. 29-31, plates. xxviii and xli, and M. Sandman, *Texts from the Time of Akhenaten (Bibliotheca Aegyptiaca VIII)* (Brussels, 1938), pp. 93-96. There are a great many translations in various languages. I have given that of M. Lichtheim, *Ancient Egyptian Literature,* Vol. 2, pp. 96-100, because it is particularly appealing to me. She notes three other English translations in her introduction to this hymn. The numbers included in the translation given here I have taken from the text itself.

(*Doc. II.7d.*) The hieroglyphic transcription of the Hymn to Ptah found in Berlin Papyrus 3048 (dating to the time of Ramesses VI), was given by W. Wolf, "Der Berliner Ptah-Hymnus (P 3048, II-XII)," *ZÄS,* Vol. 64 (1929), pp. 17-44. A German translation with notes is also included. See as well the more recent translation of Assmann, *Ägyptische Hymnen,* pp. 322-33, 589-92. Many passages from this hymn are quoted and discussed by M. Sandman Holmberg, *The God Ptah* (Lund, 1946), see Index (under "Papyrus"). The letters used for the main divisions are those given by Wolf.

(*Doc. II.7e.*) The pertinent texts from Esna for the hymns of Neith and Khnum are found in S.

Sauneron, *Esna*, Vol. 3: *Le temple d'Esna* (Cairo, 1968): Texts No. 206, pp. 28-34; No. 319, pp. 243-46; No. 378, pp. 349-53; and No. 394, pp. 375-76. For a French translation with commentary on the pertinent parts of the hymns, see *Esna*, Vol. 5: *Les fêtes religieuses d'Esna aux derniers siècles du Paganisme* (Cairo, 1962): No. 206, pp. 253-71; No. 319, pp. 238-42; No. 378, pp. 212-19; and No. 394, pp. 206-07.

After the completion of this multiple document, I acquired the very useful work of A. Barucq and F. Daumas, *Hymnes et prières de l'Égypte ancienne* (Paris, 1980). It contains good general and special introductions, with a helpful bibliography. It has complete French translations of the following hymns I have included in Document II.7: Doc. II.7a, pp. 91-97; II.7b[1], 191-201; II.7b[2], 187-91; II.7b[3], 206-33; II.7b[4], 255-61; II.7d, 389-407. In addition, it contains many more hymns.

# Document II.7a

## The Great Hymn to Osiris

(1) Adoration of Osiris by the overseer of the cattle of [Amun], [Amen]mose, and the lady Nefertari. He says:

Hail to you, Osiris,
Lord of eternity (nḥḥ), king of gods,
Of many names, of holy forms,
Of secret rites in temples!
Noble of ka he presides in Djedu (Busiris),
He is rich in sustenance (2) in Sekhem (Letopolis),
Lord of acclaim in Andjty (the ninth nome of Lower Egypt),
Foremost in offerings in On (Heliopolis).
Lord of remembrance in the Hall of Justice (*lit.* the Two Truths),
Secret ba of the lord of the cavern,
Holy in White-Wall (Memphis and its nome),
Ba of Re, his very body.
Who reposes in (3) Hnes (Heracleopolis Magna),
Who is worshipped in the *narat*-tree,
That grew up to bear his ba.
Lord of the palace in Khmun (Hermopolis),
Much revered in Shashotep (Hypselis),
Eternal Lord who presides in Abydos,
Who dwells distant in the graveyard,
Whose name endures in peoples' (4) mouths.

# ANCIENT EGYPTIAN SCIENCE

Oldest in the joined Two Lands,
Nourisher before the Nine Gods,
Potent spirit among the spirits.
Nun has given him his waters,
Northwind journeys south to him,
Sky makes wind before his nose,
That his heart be satisfied.
(5) Plants sprout by his wish,
Earth grows its food for him,
Sky and its stars obey him.
The great portals open for him.
Lord of acclaim in the southern sky,
Sanctified in the northern sky,
(6) The imperishable stars are under his rule,
The unwearying stars are his abode.
One offers to him by Geb's command,
The Nine Gods adore him,
Those in *dat* (the Netherworld) kiss the ground,
Those on high bow down.
The ancestors rejoice (7) to see him,
Those yonder are in awe of him.

.... (9) ....
The eldest of the Nine Gods,
Who set Maat through the Two Shores,
Placed the son on his father's seat.
.... (10) ....
Who vanquishes the evil-plotters,
Whose heart is firm when he crushes the rebels.

Geb's heir (in) the kingship of the Two Lands,
Seeing his worth he gave (it) to him,
To lead (11) the land to good fortune.
He placed the land into his hand,

Its water, its wind,
Its plants, all its cattle.
All that flies, all that alights,
Its reptiles and its desert game,
Were given to the (12) son of Nut,
And the Two Lands are content with it.
.... (13) ....
He is the leader of all the gods
Effective in the Word of Command,

....

His sister was his guard,
She who drives off the foes,
(14) Who stops the deeds of the disturber
By the power of her utterance.
The clever-tongued whose speech fails not,
Effective in the word of command,
Mighty Isis who protected her brother,
Who sought him without wearying,
(15) Who roamed the land lamenting,
Not resting till she found him,
Who made a shade with her plumage,
Created breath with her wings.
Who jubilated, joined her brother,
(16) Raised the weary one's inertness,
Received the seed, bore the heir,
Raised the child in solitude,
His abode unknown.
Who brought him when his arm was strong
Into the broad hall of (17) Geb.

The Ennead was jubilant:
"Welcome, Son of Osiris,
Horus, firm-hearted, justified,
Son of Isis, heir of Osiris!"

The Council of Maat assembled for him
The Ennead, the All-Lord himself,
The Lords of Maat, united in her.
(18) Who eschew wrongdoing,
They were seated in the hall of Geb,
To give the office to its lord,
The kingship to its rightful owner.
Horus was found justified,
His father's rank was given him,
He came out crowned (19) by Geb's command,
Received the rule of the two shores.
....

# Document II.7b

## Hymns to Amon-Re

### Document II.7b[1]
### A

(I,1) Adoration to Amon-Re, the bull who resides in On (Heliopolis), chief of all gods, the good god, the beloved one who gives life to everything warm and to all good cattle.

Hail to you, Amon-Re,
Lord of the thrones of the Two Lands, presiding over Thebes,
Kamatef (Bull of his Mother), presiding over his fields,
Far-strider, presiding over Upper Egypt,
Lord of the Madjoi (Nubia) and ruler of Punt,
Eldest of heaven, first-born of earth,
Lord of what is (i.e. of all that exists),
(I,5) Enduring in all things, enduring in all things.

Unique in his nature among the gods,
Beautiful bull of the Ennead, chief of all gods,
Lord of maat (truth *or* order), father of the gods,
Who made mankind and created beasts,
Lord of what is, who created the fruit tree (*or* the plants of life),
Who made herbage and caused cattle to live.

Divine Power whom Ptah made,
Beautiful youth, (II,1) beloved one,
To whom the gods give praise,
Who made the things below and the things above,
Who illuminates the Two Lands,
Who traverses the heaven in peace.

....

The chief one who made the entire earth,
More distinctive as to plans than any god,
In whose beauty the gods rejoice,
To whom is given jubilation in Per-wer,
And [ceremonial] appearances in Per-nezer,
Whose fragrance the gods love when he comes from Punt,
Rich in perfume (II,5) when he comes from Madjoi,
The one beautiful of face who comes [from] God's land,

....

Jubilation to you who made the gods,
Raised the heaven and laid down the ground.

B

(III,1) He who awakes in health, Min-Amon,
Lord of eternity *(nḥḥ)*, who made everlastingness *(ḏt)*,
Lord of praise, presiding over the Ennead
.... (IV,1) ....

## C

Hail to you, O Re, lord of maat,
Whose shrine is hidden, lord of the gods,
Khepri in the midst of his bark,
Who gave commands (*lit.* decreed words) and the gods
came into being.
Atum, who made the people,
Distinguished their natures, made their life,
And separated colors (skin pigments?), one from
another,
.... (IV,5) ....
Lord of Understanding *(si³)*, with Command *(ḥw)* in his
mouth,
....
In whose beauty the gods rejoice;
(V,1) Their hearts live when they see him.

## D

O Re, adored in Karnak,
Great in appearances in the Benben-house,
The pillared-one (i.e. the Heliopolitan), lord of the New
Moon Feast,
For whom the Feasts of Sixth Day and
Third-Quarter-Month Day are held.
.... (VI,1) ....

## E

You are the sole one who made (VI,3) everything that
is,
Solitary sole [one], who made that which is,
From whose eyes mankind came forth,
And on whose mouth the gods came into being,
He who made herbage that cattle might live,

And the fruit trees (*or* plants of life) for the sun-people
(i.e. man),
Who made that [on which] the fish (VI,5) of the river
may live,
And the birds which belong to the sky,
He who gives breath to that which is in the egg,
He who causes to live the offspring of the serpent,
And makes that on which gnats may live,
And worms and flies in like manner;
He who makes provision for the mice in their holes,
And gives life to flying things (*or* beetles?) in every
tree (*or* wood).
Hail to you who did all of these things,
The solitary, sole one, with his many arms;
(VII,1) ....
The gods bow (VII,5) down to your majesty
And exalt the might of him who produced them,
Rejoicing at the approach of him who begot them.
They say to you: "Come in peace (i.e. Welcome),
Father of the fathers of all the gods (i.e. the Ogdoad or
first gods),
Who raised the heavens and laid down the ground,
Who made what is and created what exists."
.... (VIII,1) ....

## F

Hail to you (VIII,2) who made all that is,
Lord of maat, father of the gods,
Who made man and created beasts,
Lord of the grain,
Who made nourishment for the beasts of the desert.

....

(VIII,5) The chief of the Great Ennead,
The solitary, sole one, without his peer

....
And living on maat every day.
.... (IX,1) ....

## G

Sole king (IX,3) among the gods,
Rich in names, the number of which nobody knows,
Rising in the eastern horizon,
And setting in the western horizon
....

### Document II.7b[2]

(1) Praising Amun when he rises as Harakhti, by the overseer of the works of Amun, Seth, and by the overseer of the works of Amun, Horus. They say:

Hail to you, beautiful Re, every day, who rises (2) at dawn without ceasing, Khepri who wearies himself with work. Your rays are in the face [of every one] without [his] knowing it. Electrum is not like (i.e. not so bright as) your radiance. (3) You are a Ptah, you who have fashioned your body, the shaper who is not [himself] shaped, the unique one who runs through eternity on high, [through] ways by the millions [which] carry his image; (4) just as is your radiance, so is the radiance of heaven, [but] your color is more sparkling than its surface.

When you cross the sky all faces see you, [but] when you depart you are hidden from their (5) faces .... One brief day and you have raced a course of millions and hundreds of thousands of leagues (itrw). (6) Every day under you is [but] an instant, and you set when it passes .... (8) ....Hail to you sun disk of the daytime, creator of all and maker of their living, great falcon (9) with bright plumage, who came into being in order to lift himself up and to create himself, one who was not born, Horus, the first-born in the midst of the sky-goddess, for whom they jubilate (10) when he rises, as well as when he sets, the fashioner of that which the earth produces, the Khnum and Amun of man, ... beneficent mother (11) of the gods and man, a patient craftsman, who becomes weary with [the toil of] making them without number ....

### Document II.7b[3]

Ninth Chapter. The Ennead, which came forth from Nun. They unite at (II,3) the sight of you, great of majesty, Lord of lords, fashioning himself, the Lord of the Two Ladies .... (II,4) .... His eyes gleam, his ears are opened. All bodies are clothed [in light] when (II,5) his brightness comes. The sky is gold, Nun is lapis lazuli, the earth is overspread with emerald, when he arises in it. The gods see (II,6), their temples are opened, men come to see, seeing by means of him .... (II,10). There is nothing made without him, great god, life of the Ennead.

Tenth Chapter .... [Here Thebes is praised as the place where creation was enacted in the first time, i.e. where water and land first existed; see above, Chapter Two, note 3.]

Twentieth Chapter. How you sail (II,16), Harakhti, doing your customary routine of yesterday in the course of each day, maker of years, one who forms the months. Days, nights, and (II,17) hours are according to his march. You are created (i.e. renewed) this day beyond yesterday ....

Fortieth Chapter. (II,26) Crafting himself, no one knows his shapes, a fair color, becoming holy, building his [own] images, creating himself, beautiful Power,

(II,27) making beautiful his heart, uniting his seed with his body in order to bring into being his egg within his secret self, becoming a form, (II,28) image of birth, completely himself ....

Fiftieth Chapter .... (III,1) Adoration to your majesty. The Disk of the sky shines for your face. The Nile flows from its cavern for your primordial gods. Earth is provided for your statue. (III,2) Yours alone is what Geb causes to grow, your name is strong, your might is weighty .... [Amun's might is further described in terms of a hawk, a bull, and a lion.]

Sixtieth Chapter .... (III,7) .... his boundary was strong when he was on the earth throughout the whole land and up to the sky. (III,8) The gods begged their sustenance from him. He gave them food from his possessions, lord of fields, and *idbw-* and *nḥb*-lands .... (III,10) Sated (*or* satisfied, i.e. satisfactorily established?) was the royal cubit, which measures blocks of stone. Stretching the cord over the ... of the ground, establishing the Two Lands upon its foundation, and shrines and temples ....

Eightieth Chapter. The Ogdoad (III,23) were your first form, until you completed them, and you were one. Secret is your body among the great ones, concealing yourself as (III,24) Amun at the head of the gods. You made your transformation as Tatenen in order to cause the primordial gods to come into being. Exalting (III,25) your beauty (i.e. becoming?) as Kemphis, you removed yourself as one who dwells in the sky, being established as Re .... (III,26) .... You came into being when there was no other being. No land was without you on the first occasion. All gods came into being after you ....

[Nintieth Chapter.] (IV,1) The Ennead was still joined with your members [in the beginning]. As for your form, all gods were still joined to your body. You emerged first. You began before [all], Amun hiding (IV,2) his name from the gods, great aged one, older than these, Tatenen who shaped himself as Ptah. The toes (or nails) (IV,3) of his limbs were the Ogdoad. Rising as Re from Nun, he became young again. Spitting .... Shu and Tefenet, (IV,4) joined with his might, rising on his throne according to the granting of his heart (i.e. according to the desire of his heart). He ruled everything that existed by his power (?). He arranged the kingdom of eternity (nḥḥ) (IV,5) down to everlastingness (ḏt), established as sole lord. His form shone at the first time. Everything was silent on account of his majesty. [Then] he cackled, (IV,6) being the Great Cackler, in the place where he was created, he alone. He began to speak in the midst of silence. He opened all eyes (IV,7) and made them see. He commenced to cry when the earth was inert. His cry spread about when there was no one else in existence but him. (IV,8) He brought forth all things which exist. He caused them to live. He made all men understand the way to go and their hearts came alive when they saw him ....

(IV,9) Hundredth Chapter. "Coming into being" (i.e Creation) began in the first time and Amun came into being in the [very] beginning. [Hence] his form was unknown. No god came into being before him; there was no other (IV,10) god with him [to whom] he might tell his form. He had no mother to produce his name and had no father who begot him [and thus] could say "This is I" (or "He is mine"). Shaping (IV,11) his own egg, mysterious force of births who created his [own] beauty, divine god who created himself. All [other] gods came into being after he began [to make] himself.

(IV,12) Two-hundredth Chapter. Secret of forms, gleaming of shapes, marvelous god, multiple of forms, all other gods boast (IV,13) of him in order to magnify themselves through his beauty, according as he is divine. Re himself is united with his body. He is the great one who is in On (i.e. Heliopolis). He is called (IV,14) Tatenen and Amun who came forth from Nun. He leads the people. Another of his forms is the Ogdoad. The begetter *(pꜣ wtt)* of the primordial (IV,15) gods *(pꜣwtyw)* who brought Re to birth. He completed *(tm-f)* himself as Atum *(tm)*, a single body with him. He is the All-Lord, the beginning of that which is (i.e. of everything that exists). His soul, they say, is that (IV,16) which is in heaven, ... his body is in the West. His statue is in Hermonthis, (IV,17) exalting his appearances.

One is Amun, hiding himself from them, concealing himself from the gods, so that his [very] color (*or* complexion) is not known. He is far (IV,18) from heaven, he is absent (?) from the Netherworld, [so that] no gods know his true form. His image is not displayed (?) in writings ....

Three-hundredth Chapter. All gods are three: Amun, Re, and Ptah, and there is none like them (i.e. equal to them). His name is "hidden" *(imn)* as (IV,22) Amun, he is Re in face (i.e. appearance), and his body is Ptah. Their cities are on the earth: Thebes, Heliopolis, and Memphis, enduring for an eternity ....

[Six-hundredth Chapter.] Understanding *(siꜣ)* is his heart, Command *(ḥw)* is his lips, (V,17) his ka, every existing thing which is in his mouth. When he enters the two caverns (V,18) which are under his feet, the Nile comes forth from the grotto under his sandals. (V,19) His ba is Shu, his heart is Tefnut (?). He is

Harakhti who dwells in (V,20) heaven; his right eye is day and his left eye is night. He [thus] leads (V,21) people to every way. His body is Nun, and he who is in it is the Nile, giving (V,22) birth to whatever is, and causing to live whatever exists. His warm air is breath for every nostril (V,23). Fate and fortune are with him for everybody (i.e., he has within himself the fate and fortune of everyone). His wife is the fertile field; he impregnates her; his seed is the fruit tree and his fluid is the grain ....

## Document II.7b[4]

[1] This august god, Lord of all Gods, Amon-Re, Lord of the Thrones of the Two Lands, He who is at the fore of Karnak.

[2] August Soul *(b¹)*, who came into being at the beginning, the Great God who lives on Truth, the first primeval one who fashioned the [3] primeval gods, he out of whom every other god came into being.

The Unique one, who created what existed, who at the first time created the earth.

[4] Mysterious of births, numerous of appearances, whose secret image is not known.

August power, who calls forth love, [5] Majestic one, rich in his appearances, Lord of magnificence, with mighty forms, out of whose form [6] came every form, he who first came into being when nothing existed but him.

He who gave light to the earth in the first time, the Noble sundisk [7] with light-producing rays, Radiating one [such that] when he appears every countenance comes alive.

When he sails the sky, he is not weary.

[8] Morning upon morning his routine is fixed.

Ancient One who in the morning arises as a youth who brings forth (i.e. reaches to) [9] the limits of eternity *(nḥḥ)*, who circles the sky, passing through the Netherworld *(dꞋt)* in order to give light to the Two Lands for that which he has created.

[10] Divine god who formed himself, who made heaven and earth in his heart.

Ruler of rulers, Greatest [11] of the great, the Noble one who is older than the gods.

Young Bull with sharp horns, [12] before whose mighty name the Two Lands tremble.

Eternity comes under his might, he who reaches the end of everlastingness.

[13] Great God who created being, who seized the Two Lands with his might.

Ram-headed one with lofty form, [14] more gracious than all the gods, a lion of terrible aspect when he lifts up both *wadjat*-eyes,

[15] Lord of flames against his enemies, the great Watery Abyss *(nw)*, who manifests himself at his hour to [16] make live what comes forth from his potter's wheel.

He who wanders about the sky, who circles in the Netherworld, giving light to the earth as he gave it [17] yesterday.

Lord of Might, of unapproachable majesty, his rays keep his body hidden.

His right [18] eye and his left eye are the sun-disk and the Moon, the sky and the earth are full of the beauty of his light.        [19] Benevolent king, who is never weary, [but has] a strong heart at rising and setting.

Mankind came forth from [20] his two divine eyes, the gods from the speech of his mouth, he who makes food, who creates nourishment, who shapes [21] all that is.

Everlasting one, who wanders through the years without end to his lifetime.

Ancient one [22] who becomes young, who traverses eternity.

When old he makes himself young.

With numerous pairs of eyes and [23] with many pairs of ears, he who guides millions when he shines.

Lord of Life, who gives to whom he wishes.

The circumference of [24] the earth is under his charge, who gives a command and it happens without opposition, whose work will never perish.

[25] He whose name is pleasing, whose love is sweet.

In the morning all faces pray to him.

[26] He is great of terror, he whom every god fears.

The young bull who repulses [27] the adversary, strong of arm, he who strikes down his enemy.

This god who created the earth according to his plans.

Soul (*b?*) [28] who shines with both *wadjat*-eyes.

He who manifests himself while coming into being, he who becomes the Holy One, without being known.

[29] He is the King who creates kings, who ties together lands with the order he has made.

The gods and the goddesses [30] bow down before his might because [their] reverence of him is so great.

He who came in the beginning accomplishes the end.

He has created [31] lands according to his plans.

He whose forms are mysterious is he whom nobody knows, who has hidden himself from all the gods, [32] who drew himself into the disk, the Unknown One, who conceals himself from those who came out of him.

Radiant torch, [33] Great of Light, one sees because he is seen.

He is seen the whole day [34] without being understood therein.

When he dawns, all faces adore him, [35] the one brilliant in appearances in the midst of the Ennead.

His form is that of every god.

The flood comes, [36] the Northwind proceeds upstream in this mysterious god, he who makes decrees for millions of millions.

[37] His decisions do not waver, his word is stable, his decrees are efficacious and do not ever fail.

[38] He grants existence, he doubles the years of him who is in his favor, he is a good protector of him whom [39] he has placed in his heart, he is the supporter for ever and ever; King of Upper and Lower Egypt, Amon-Re, King of the Gods, Lord of the Heaven and the Earth, of the Waters and the Mountains, [40] who created the land by means of his forms, he is greater and more elevated (*lit.* more White-crown-like) than all of the primeval gods of the first time ....

# Document II.7c

# The Great Hymn to the Aten

(1) Adoration of *Re-Harakhti who rejoices in*

*Lightland In his name Shu who is Aten*, living forever; the great living Aten who is in jubilee, the lord of all that the Disk encircles, lord of sky, lord of earth, lord of the house-of-Aten in Akhet-Aten; (and of) the King of Upper and Lower Egypt ... *Neferkheprure, Sole one of Re*, the Son of Re who lives by Maat .... and his beloved great Queen, the Lady of the Two Lands, *Nefer-nefru-Aten Nefertiti* ...; (2) he says:

Splendid you rise in heaven's lightland.
O living Aten, creator of life!
When you have dawned in eastern lightland,
You fill every land with your beauty.
....
Your rays embrace the lands,
To the limit of all that you made.
.... (4) ....
Earth brightens when you dawn in lightland,
When you shine as Aten of daytime;
As you dispel the dark,
As you cast your rays,
The Two Lands are in festivity.
Awake they stand on their feet.
You have roused them;
.... (5) ....
All beasts browse on their herbs;
Trees, herbs are sprouting,
Birds fly from their nests,
Their wings greeting your ka.
All flocks frisk on their feet,
All that fly up and alight,
(6) They live when you dawn for them.
....

# ANCIENT EGYPTIAN SCIENCE

Who makes seed grow in women.
Who creates people from sperm;
Who feeds the son in his mother's womb,
Who soothes him to still his tears.
Nurse in the (7) womb,
Giver of breath,
To nourish all that he made.
....

How many are your deeds,
Though hidden from sight,
(8) O Sole God beside whom there is none!
You made the earth as you wished, you alone,
All people, herds, and flocks;
All upon earth that walk on legs,
All on high that fly on wings,
The lands of Khor and Kush,
The land of Egypt.
You set every man in his place;
Everyone has his food,
His lifetime is counted.
Their tongues differ in speech,
Their characters (9) likewise;
Their skins are distinct,
For you distinguished the peoples.

You made Hapy (the Nile god) in *dat* (the Netherworld),
You bring him [as flood waters] when you will,
To nourish the people;
....
You made a heavenly Hapy (i.e. rain) descend for them;
(10) He makes waves on the mountains like the sea
....

Your rays nourish all fields,
When you shine they live, they grow for you;
You made the seasons to foster all that you made,
(11) Winter to cool them, heat that they taste you.
You made the far sky to shine therein,
To behold all that you made;
You alone, shining in your form of living Aten,
Risen, radiant, distant, near.
You made millions of forms *(ḫprw)* from yourself alone,
Towns, villages, fields, the river's course;
....

(12)....
〈Those on〉 earth come from your hand as you made them,
When you have dawned they live,
When you set they die;
You yourself are lifetime, one lives by you.
....

# Document II.7d

## Hymn to Ptah

### A

(1) Adoration of Ptah, the father of the gods, Tatenen,
The eldest of the primordial gods, in the morning.

### B

(1) Say: Hail to you, Ptah, the father of the gods, Tatenen,
The eldest of the primordial gods,

....
(10) Lightgiver who caused the gods to live,

....
(15) Who travels the sky and passes through the Netherworld,

....
(19) He who begot himself when no being had [yet] come into being,
Who crafted the earth from the plans of his heart.
Whose forms came into being [from himself].
You are he who has fashioned every thing that is, who has produced and formed that which exists.

C

(1) Hail to you, Ptah-Tatenen,
Great god whose image is hidden,

....
(4) Father of the father of all the gods,

....
(9) May you awaken in peace, you who carries Nut and lifts up Geb,

....
(12) May you awaken in peace, you [as] Khnum and Mut who bore the gods,
Who begot and made all eyes (i.e. men) and made their provisions of life.
....

D

....
(3) Hail to you in front of your primordial gods,
Whom you have made after you came into being as a god,
(5) Body who has modeled his own body,

When the sky had not [yet] come into being and the earth had not [yet] come into being,
When no flood had arisen.
You have knotted the land,
You have assembled your body and have counted your members,
(10) You have found yourself to be the Sole One, who has made his [own] place,
God who has fashioned the Two Lands,
You have no father who engendered you when you came into being,
You have no mother who bore you,
You who are your own Khnum,
(15) The provider from whom [every] provision has come forth.
You stood on the land when it was inert,
[You] by whom it was later put together,
You in your form of Tatenen,
In your form of Uniter of the Two Lands,
(20) That which your mouth has engendered and your hands have fashioned,
You have drawn it forth from Nun
By means of your two hands in imitation of your beauty;
Your son (i.e. the sun), ancient in his forms,
Has chased away the darkness and the shadows,
(25) By means of the rays of his two eyes.
....
(30) You have set him right along his secret ways.
His two barks (day and night) travel along the sky
By means of the wind which comes forth from his (! your?) mouth.
Your feet are on the ground and your head is in the sky

In your form of "He who is in the Netherworld".

....

(42) Your power lifts up water into the sky.
The exhalations of your mouth are the clouds.

....

(63) Your right eye is the sun disk, your left eye the moon.
Your guides are the unwearying stars (i.e. the non-circumpolar ones).

....

E

(1) Hail, let us praise him,
The god who has lifted high the sky, who causes his sun disk to sail forth into the belly of Naunet
And leads him into the belly of Nut,
In his name of Re.

(5) Hail, let us praise him,
Who fashioned the gods, the people, and the animals (?),
He who made all the lands and the ocean shore,
In his name as Crafter (or Builder) of the Earth.

Hail, let us praise him,
(10) Who brings the Nile out of its cavern,
Who makes green the fruit trees (or plants of life)
And makes provision for those who came forth from him,
In his name of Nun.

Hail, let us praise him,
(15) Who sets in motion (or lifts up) Nun (i.e. water) into the sky

And makes water come forth upon the mountains,
In order to bring other people to life,
In his name of Maker of Life.

Hail, let us praise him,
(20) Who made the Netherworld in its plan,
Who overcomes the heat of the bas in their caverns,
In his name of King of the Two Lands.

Hail, let us praise him,
King of eternity *(nḥḥ)* and everlastingness *(ḏt)*,
(25) Lord of life in the Lake of Knives, chief of the Desert of the Land of the Dead,
In his name of Chief of the Netherworld.

....

## F

(1) O, You who have opened the Way.

....

(3) O, You who arise as Re,
O, You who come forth as Khepri, who lives among the dwellers in the horizon.
You have awakened them,
That they may point out to you the correct way of Nut,
In your coming forth as the Great Form in order to make the plans of eternity *(nḥḥ)* forever *(ḏt)*.

## G

(1) Come let us celebrate him.
Let us praise his august image
In all his beautiful names,
Child who is born every day.

(5) Come let us celebrate him,
Let us praise his august image
In all his beautiful names,
Old one who dwells at the limits of eternity *(nḥḥ)*.

Come let us celebrate him,
(10) Let us praise his august image
In all of his beautiful names,
Elder one who will continue to travel everlastingly *(ḏt)*.

....

(32) Ba of the Lord of years, who gives life to whom he wishes.

Come let us jubilate him,
Let us praise his august image
In all his beautiful names,
You who commands and it will be done without opposition.

### H

(1) Hail to you, the ways are opened to you,
The paths of everlastingness are opened up for you,
Founded for you are the sky and the earth, the Netherworld and Nun.
You have made plans for those who are in them (i.e. these areas)
(5) You give life, you set the years (i.e. life times) for men and for gods.

....

(9) You come and go, [in] both heavens ... as living ba.

....

(13) Your eldest son, he worships you
In your form "More beautiful than the [other] gods",

In your form "He is beautiful as to form",
As your son has said to you:
"Mighty is my father, from whom I have come forth,
The Lord of mankind, who created me in Nun,
He who has lifted high the heaven for me and supported the earth for me,
(20) Who has caused me to travel along the body of Nut,
And has led me on the secret ways."
....

## I

....
(5) Hail to you, Ptah,
Hail to your gods, who come into being from your body,
How great are you in respect to (i.e. compared to) your primordial gods.
....

(13) They have been with him for an eternity *(nḥḥ)*, they will be with him time everlasting *(ḏt)*.
...

## K

....
(9) Heka (magic) has power over the gods;
His fame (*or* power) is great under the Ennead.
....

(23) And their [majesty] caused his (i.e. Ptah's) son Re to ascend
To protect men and gods
By the skill of his power.

L

(1) Hail, Come, and protect the King of Upper and Lower Egypt, Ramesses IX, L. P. H.
As you protect the gods who came into being in this land,
Whose king you were....
(7) Eternity *(nḥḥ)* belongs to you; it is your possession.

# Document II.7e

# Cosmogonies at the Temple of Esna

### Text 206: Neith

(1) Father of the fathers, mother of the mothers, the divinity who began to come into being in the beginning was in the midst of the Abyss. She appeared out of herself while the land was [still] in the shadows and no land had [yet] appeared and no plant had sprouted .... She turned herself into a cow so that no divinity wherever he would be could recognize her. Then she changed herself into (*lit.* renewed her appearance as) a lates-fish (2) and started off. She made luminescent the glances of her eyes, and light came into being. Then she said: "Let this place (where I am) become for me a platform of land in the midst of the Abyss in order that I might stand on it." And this place became a platform of land in the midst of the Abyss, just as she said. And [thus] came into being "the land of the waters" (=Esna), which is also Sais ....

Everything which her heart conceived came into being immediately. (3) Thus she felt happy about this emergence [of the land] and so Egypt came into being in this happiness.

She created thirty gods by pronouncing their names, one by one, and she became happy when she saw them. They said: "Hail to you, Mistress of divinities, our mother, who has brought us into being. You have made our names before we knew them (i.e. yet had cognizance of them) ... you have made [for us] the land upon which we can stand, you have separated [for us] the night from the day .... How very beneficial is everything which comes from your heart, O Sole One, created in the beginning. Eternity *(nḥḥ)* and everlastingness *(dt)* pass before your face .... [(4) Then Neith establishes the gods on the emergent land, and they ask (5) what is going to be created.]

Neith then said: "I shall cause you to know what is coming into being. Let us count the four spirits *(ʾḥw)*. Let us give form to what is in our bodies (i.e. in our hearts?) and then let us pronounce our forms. So, we shall recognize everything the same day." Everything she said took place, and the eighth hour (i.e. the culminating time) occurred in the space of a moment.

The Ahet-cow (*or* Ihet-cow; *here* Neith) began to think about what she was going to create. She said: "An august god will come into being today. When he opens his eyes, light will come into being; when he closes them, (6) darkness will come into being. People will come into being from the tears of his eye, gods from the spittle of his lips. I will strengthen him by my strength, I will make him effective by my efficacy, I will make him vigorous by my vigor. His children will rebel against him, but they will be beaten on his behalf and struck down on his behalf, for he is my son issued from my body, and he will be king of this land forever *(dt)*. I will protect him with my arms .... (7) I am going to tell you his name: it will be Khepri in the morning and Atum in the evening; and he will be the radiating god in his rising forever, in his name of Re, every day."

Then these gods said: "We are ignorant (ḥm-n) of the things we have heard." So the "Eight" (ḥmnw) became the name of these gods (i.e. the Ogdoad) and also the name of this city (i.e. "Eighttown", i.e. Hermopolis or Ashmunein).

So this god was born from the excretions that came forth from the body of Neith and which she placed in the body of this [primordial] egg .... (8) .... When it broke the shell, it was Re who was hidden in the midst of the Abyss in his name of Amun the Elder and who fashioned the gods and the goddesses with his rays in his name of Khnum.

His mother, the cow goddess, called out loudly: "Come, come, you whom I have created. Come, come, you whom I have conceived. Come, come, (9) you whom I have caused to come into being .... I am your mother, the cow goddess." This god then came forth, his mouth open, his arms opened toward this goddess .... And this day [of the sun's birth] then became the beautiful day of the beginning of the year (tp rnpt).

Then he cried in the Abyss when he did not see his mother, the cow goddess, and mankind came into being from the tears of his eye; and he salivated when he saw her again, and the gods came into being from the saliva of his lips.

(10) These primordial gods [now] rest in their shrines; they have been pronounced (dm) [by creative word] just as this goddess conceived them in her heart ....

They (the ancestor gods) thrust aside (11) a wad

of spittle from her mouth which she had produced in the Abyss, and it was transformed into a serpent of 120 cubits, which was named Apep (Apophis). Its heart conceived the revolt against Re, its cohorts coming from its eyes.

Thoth emerged from his (i.e. Re's) heart in a moment of bitterness (*dḥr*), which accounts for his name of Thoth (*dḥwty*). He speaks with his father, who sent him against the revolt, in his name of Lord of the Word of God. And this is how Thoth, Lord of Khmun, came into being, in this place, as well as that of the Eight-gods of the first company of gods.

.... [Then Neith goes to her city of Esna (i.e. Sais) with her son to establish his name there. She will suckle him until he is strong enough to massacre those plotting against him. Then we are told that the seven propositions that she declared in the course of creation became seven divinities] .... (13) And so came into being the Seven Proposition-Goddesses of Methyer ....

Text 319: To Khnum
(13) Praise, praise to your good countenance,
Khnum, our Lord of All (i.e. to the Limits),
Sacred god who created (14) all his aspects in just account.
....
See, you are the divine god who organizes the country by his work.

Your are my ruler and I am your servant.
....
[My] nose lives from the breath of your mouth.
.... (16) ....

You are the [All-]Powerful, rich in aspects, great in favor, who acts according to your perfection.
You have modeled men on the potter's wheel,
You have made the gods,
You have modeled large and small cattle,
You have formed everything upon your (17) wheel, each day,
[in] your name of Khnum the Potter.

You have distinguished the king in the womb from among those you have created
In order that he administer the universe to the limits [of time].
.... (20) ....

How great is your might among the gods and how great is the awe of you among the Ennead ....

## Text 378
### Another Hymn to Khnum
(9) You are the Lord of Esna,
The god of the [potter's] wheel,
Who turned the gods [on it],
Who modeled men as well as animals [on it];
....
No god can equal him, the best-beloved ram,
Who made that which is and that which is not,
(10) Who bore the gods and engendered the goddesses.

You are the august god who came into being in the beginning,
The one whom one goddess accompanies, the uraeus serpent,
The mysterious one whose form no one knows,

The secret god whose appearance no one knows,
The one who came forth from the Abyss,
Who arose in the horizon as a flame.
The One under whose feet the flood rises from two
caverns.
The One from whom wafts the sweet North Wind for
the nostrils of gods and men.
....

(12) You are the infant who spreads his light at dawn,
....
You illuminate the Two Lands with your two eyes.
His right eye is the sun and his left is the moon;
And he has created creatures in [the heaven] and on
earth, in the inferior world and in the Abyss.

(13) You are Tatenen, more eminent than the gods,
.... (14) ....
All of this he has made in totality,
And there is no god who could do what he has done,
He, this august god,
Khnum-Re, Lord of Esna.

You are the god who lifted the sky,
Heh who supported Nut,
Shu, the eldest son of Atum, (15) the solitary one,
Who has produced everything which exists,
Who has created the light by his two eyes,
To give light to the Two Lands,
....
Who has made life (16) for all those he has created.
....

## Text 394

(23) Another hymn to Khnum. To be said:
Hail to you, Khnum-Re, Lord of Esna,
Ptah-Tatenen, who has fashioned the primordial gods,
Great god, who came into being at the very beginning,
Magnificent ram, at the first time.
He lifted the earth and supported the sky,
And he diffused the light there in the form of radiance.
He installed the soul of the spirits in the midst of the waters (?).
....
He acted the god (25) when he began to come into being,
....
The most significant of the significant, who is greater than all the gods,
Mysterious of aspect, who is eminent (26) above the gods,
Modeler of the modelers,
Eldest of the primordial gods,
Father of the fathers, mother of the mothers,
Who made the superior beings and created the inferior beings,
The august ram, who made the rams,
Khnum who made the Khnums,
....
Having made (27) the cities and separated the countries,
Having created the Two Lands and made firm the mountains,
He made man on the [potter's] wheel,
He bore the gods, in order to fill up (i.e. populate) the land and the circle of the great ocean,
Coming in time to bring to life all those who came forth from his wheel,

Making herbage to provide for cattle and the tree of
life for men,
He comes forth at the right time without (28) cease.

....

# Document II.8: Introduction

## *The Destruction of Apep*

This work from which our document has been taken is the third and longest text to be found in Papyrus British Museum No. 10188, a papyrus, which, at the latest, dates from the fourth century B.C.; it is written in Middle Egyptian but shows evidence of having been artificially composed in that idiom, since it includes some tell-tale Late-Egyptian expressions.[1] Faulkner, the modern editor of this papyrus, suggests that it was a collection of religious texts originally written for a temple library.[2]

The interest of this work for us lies primarily in its fifth section entitled "The Book of Knowing the Creations *(hprw)* of Re and the Felling of Apep". The section on creation is cast as a monologue of Re. It actually appears in two not very different forms in separate parts of the work (26,21-27,5 and 28,20-29,6). I have given only the first version, but I have also included before it some ritualistic preparations for using the book against the enemies of Re and of the pharaoh (see 26,2-7).

In the part on creation we first see Re's autogenesis in the Abyss as the self-generator, Khepri, at the time when there was no other being, no sky, no earth, no ground, and no reptiles. He planned a multitude of beings in his heart and they came forth from his mouth, an apparent reference to the doctrine of the creative word. With his own genesis the very nature of coming into being itself came into being. The subsequent creation of land on which he might stand was followed in turn by the creation of Shu and Tefenet, the old views of their creation by expectoration and masturbation being put forth. Other cosmogonic acts follow: the separation of these first children from their father in the Abyss and their recovery by Re's Eye, the creation of man from the tears of his Eye, the placing of the Eye on his face (i.e. forehead) in the form of the uraeus serpent, the successive procreation of Geb and Nut by Shu and Tefenet, and of Osiris, Horus Mekhantenirti, Seth, Isis, and Nephthys by Geb and Nut, and finally the begetting of their multitudes in the land.

## Text and Study of *The Destruction of Apep*

The most important edition of this work is that included in R.O. Faulkner's edition of the papyrus: *The Papyrus Bremner-Rhind (British Museum No. 10188): Bibliotheca Aegyptiaca* III (Brussels, 1933), from column 22,1 to 32,12, pp. 42-88. Furthermore, Faulkner prepared a translation with commentary: "The Bremner-Rhind Papyrus-III [and -IV]," *JEA*, Vol. 23 (1937), pp. 166-85; Vol. 24 (1938), pp. 41-53. I have employed this translation with very few changes; e.g., I have, for the most part, stripped it of its biblical form of language and I have used "Abyss" for the non-personified form of *nw(n)* but have retained "Nun" when the reference is to the Deep as a god, the father of Re. Faulkner used "Nun" throughout. I have used the simple transcriptions of the names Re, Khepri, Tefenet, and Apep, which I have used elsewhere in the volume.

# Notes to the Introduction of Document II.8

1. Faulkner, *The Papyrus Bremner-Rhind*, p. IX.
2. *Ibid.*, p. VI.

# Document II.8

## *The Destruction of Apep*

/26/ .... (2) .... To be recited by a man who is pure and clean. You shall depict (?) every foe of Re and every foe of pharaoh, whether dead or alive, and every accused one whom he has in mind, [also] the names of their fathers, their mothers (3), and their children ..., they having been drawn in green ink on a new sheet of papyrus, their names written on their breasts, [these] having been made of wax and also bound with bonds (?) of black thread; they are to be spat upon, (4) and [they are] to be trampled with the left foot, felled with the spear and knife and cast on the fire in the melting furnace of the coppersmiths. Afterwards the name of Apep is to be burnt in a fire of bryony when Re manifests himself, when Re is at noontide, (5) and when Re sets in the West; in the first hour of the day and of the night and in the second hour of the night down to the third hour of the night; at dawn, and likewise every hour of the night and every hour of the day; at the festival of the New Moon, at the sixth-day festival, (6) at the fifteenth-day festival, and likewise at the monthly festival .... This book is to be employed in this manner which is in writing .... (7) .... It will go well with the man who makes conjurations for himself [from] this book in the presence of the august god, a true matter, [tested] a million times .... (21) ....

# ANCIENT EGYPTIAN SCIENCE

The Book of Knowing the Creations of Re and of Felling Apep. Recite: Thus spoke the Lord of All after he had come into being: "It was I who came into being as Khepri. When I came into being, 'Being' (22) came into being, and all beings came into being after I came into being; manifold were the beings which came forth from my mouth ere the sky had come into being, ere the earth had come into being, ere the ground and reptiles had been created in this place. I created [some of] them in the Abyss (23) as Inert Ones when I could as yet find no place where I could stand. I considered (?) in my heart, I surveyed with my sight, and I alone made every shape ere I had spat out Shu, ere I had expectorated Tefenet, ere there had come into being any other (24) who could act with me. I planned with my own heart and there came into being a multitude of forms of living creatures, namely the forms of children, and the forms of their children. I indeed made excitation with my /27/ fist, I copulated (1) with my hand, I spat with my own mouth; I spat out Shu, I expectorated Tefenet, and my father Nun brought them up, my Eye following after them since the aeons when they were far from me. After I had come into being as sole god, (2) there were three gods in addition to myself. I came into being in this land and Shu and Tefenet rejoiced in the Abyss, in which they were. They brought back to me my Eye with them after I had united my members; I wept over them, and that is how men came into being (3) from the tears which came forth from my Eye, for it was angry with me when it returned and found I had set another in its place, having replaced it with Glorious [Eye]. So I promoted it in my face, and when it exercised governance over (4) this entire land, its wrath died away (??), for I had replaced what had been (?) taken from it. I came forth from the roots, I created all reptiles and all that exists among them. Shu and Tefenet begot (5) Geb and Nut, and Geb and Nut begot Osiris, Horus Mekhantenirti, Seth, Isis, and Nepththys from the womb, one after another, and they begot their multitudes in this land ...."

# Document II.9: Introduction

## The *Memphite Theology*

The so-called *Memphite Theology* (this is a modern title coined by Erman) exists in only one copy, which is inscribed on a black granite stone (British Museum No. 408). The stone was prepared by the order of King Shabaka (712-698 B.C.) of the twenty-fifth dynasty, i.e. the Ethiopic dynasty, purportedly copied from an earlier "worm-eaten" copy (see line 2 of Document II.9 below). The stone has inscribed on it two horizontal lines at the top and sixty-two vertical columns, which begin on the left side of the stone (see Fig. II.53). The middle part of the text is almost completely effaced, since the stone was reused as a millstone and so a rectangular hole was cut in the middle. Grooves radiate out from the hole and the upper millstone revolved in the middle of the inscribed surface. The first person to understand the significance of the cosmogonic part of this document was Breasted, who called it the philosophy of a Memphite priest of Ptah.[1] Since his time it has been widely studied, as I note in the bibliographic paragraph below. The older view was that the text was made from an original composition that was written either in Archaic times or at least no later than the Old Kingdom. But recently F. Junge cast doubt on the advanced age of this document and instead concluded that it was composed by those who inscribed it on the stone in the twenty-fifth dynasty and that they employed archaizing language in order to enhance its and their importance.[2]   An even later study suggests a nineteenth-dynasty origin.[3] Be that as it may, it seems clear that the concept of creation by word, which is its most important doctrinal feature for us in our cosmogonic studies, reflects an old doctrine,[4] though perhaps one never elaborated to such a degree.  Again and again I have mentioned in Chapter Two and the preceding documents that the earlier traces of this doctrine seem to have solid roots in the Heliopolitan conceptions of Sia (Understanding or Intelligence) and Hu (Authoritative Utterance), and so I need not repeat this earlier history here.  Nor indeed need I summarize once more the main features of the creative activity of Ptah that is outlined in the document, for they too have been described in some detail in Chapter Two. In presenting as Document II.9 those extracts of the Shabaka Stone which are designated the *Memphite Theology*, I have given only the first two lines on the stone and the cosmogonic section itself.  The rest of the stone, or at least that which is readable, is available in the texts and translations noted below in the next section of this introduction.

## Studies and Texts of the *Memphite Theology*

The first accurate text and useful study of this work was that of J. H. Breasted, "The Philosophy of a Memphite Priest," *ZÄS*, Vol. 39 (1901), pp. 39-54. Breasted has partially reconstructed the text on the stone in accompanying plates (see Fig. II.53). The most complete study of the Shabaka Stone, which includes text, translation, and commentary, is that of K. Sethe,

*Dramatische Texte zu altägyptischen Mysterienspielen (Untersuchungen zur Geschichte und Altertumskunde Ägyptens*, Vol. 10) (Leipzig, 1928; repr. Hildesheim, 1964). For the cosmogonic part, see H. Junker, *Die Götterlehre von Memphis (Schabaka-Inschrift) (Aus den Abhandlungen der Preussischen Akademie der Wissenschaften, Jahrgang, 1939 Phil.-hist. Klasse*, Nr. 23) (Berlin, 1940). Among other studies, excerpts, and translations, we can note A. Erman, "Ein Denkmal memphitischer Theologie," *Sitzungsberichte der Königlichen Preussischen Akademie der Wissenschaften, Jahrgang 1911* (Berlin, 1911), pp. 916-50; J. H. Breasted, *The Dawn of Conscience* (New York, 1933), pp. 29-42; J. A. Wilson, "The Nature of the Universe," in H. and H. A. Frankfort, J. A. Wilson, T. Jacobsen, and W. A. Irwin, *The Intellectual Adventure of Ancient Man* (Chicago and London, 1946; Phoenix ed. 1977), pp. 55-60; M. Sandman Holmberg, *The God Ptah* (Lund and Copenhagen, 1946), *passim*, and especially pp. 19-23, 42-45; and Wilson, "Egyptian Myths, Tales, and Mortuary Texts," in J. B. Pritchard, ed., *Ancient Near Eastern Texts Relating to the Old Testament* (Princeton, 1950; 2nd ed. 1955), pp. 4-6; M. Lichtheim, *Ancient Egyptian Literature*, Vol. 1 (Berkeley/Los Angeles/London, 1975), pp. 51-57; F. Junge, "Zur Fehldatierung der sog. Denkmals memphitischer Theologie oder Der Beitrag der ägyptischen Theologie zur Geistesgeschichte der Spätzeit," *MDAIK*, Vol. 29 (1973), pp. 195-204; and H. A. Schlögel, *Der Gott Tatenen* (Freiburg, Switz., and Göttingen, 1980), pp. 110-17.

## The English Translation

In my English translation I have paid close attention to Sethe's and Junker's commentaries as well as to the English translations of Wilson and Lichtheim. The numbers in parentheses are those of the columns on the stone (except for the first two numbers which refer to the horizontal lines at the top of the stone). I have indicated in footnote 2 of the document the alternate translations of columns 53 and 54 proposed by Lichtheim on the basis of Sethe's and Junker's renderings.

# Notes to the Introduction of Document II.9

1. See the article of Breasted, "The Philosophy of a Memphite Priest," given in the bibliographical section of this Introduction.
2. See the article of Junge, "Zur Fehldatierung...," given in the bibliographical section of this Introduction.
3. See H. A. Schlögel, *Der Gott Tatenen*, pp. 110-17.
4. J. Zandee, "Das Schöpferwort im alten Ägypten," *Verbum: Essays on Some Aspects of the Religious Function of Words dedicated to Dr. H. W. Obbink (Rheno-Traiectina*, Vol. 6, 1964), pp. 33-66.

# Document II.9

## The *Memphite Theology*

(1) The living Horus: he who makes prosper the Two Lands; [the one of] the Two Ladies: he who makes prosper the Two Lands; the Golden Horus: he who makes prosper the Two Lands; the King of Upper and Lower Egypt: Neferkare; Son of Re: Sha[baka], beloved of Ptah South of his Wall, who lives like Re forever.[1] (2) His majesty copied this book anew in the House of his father Ptah South of his Wall. His majesty had found it as a work of his ancestors, which was worm-eaten, so that it could not be known from the beginning to the end. Then his majesty copied it anew so that it was in a better state than it had been in before. [He did this] in order that his name might endure and in order that his monument be made to last in the House of his father Ptah South of his Wall through the length of everlastingness *(dt)*, as a work done by the Son of Re [Shabaka] for his father Ptah-Tatenen so that he might be given life forever ....

(48) The gods who came into being in Ptah:

(49a) Ptah-upon-the-Great-Throne ...;

(50a) Ptah-Nun, the father who made (?) Atum;

(51a) Ptah-Naunet, the mother who gave birth to Atum;

(52a) Ptah-the-Great, who is the heart and the tongue of the Ennead;

(49b) [Ptah] ... who bore the gods;

(50b) [Ptah] ....

(51b) [Ptah] ....

(52b) [Ptah] ..., Nefertem at the nose of Re every day.

(53) There came into being in the heart [of Ptah] and there came into being on the tongue [of Ptah] something in the shape (i.e. form) of Atum, for Ptah is the very great one who transmitted [life] to all the gods and to their kas by means of the heart in which Horus has taken shape and by means of the tongue in which Thoth has taken shape, ... [each] (54) as [an agent or form of] Ptah.[2]

[Thus] it happened that heart and tongue gained mastery over [every] member [of the body] according to the teaching that he (Ptah) is in every body [as heart] and in every mouth [as tongue]: [i.e. in the bodies and mouths] of all gods, all men, all cattle, all creeping things, and of everything which lives. Accordingly [as heart] he thinks out (i.e. conceives) and [as tongue] he commands what he wishes [to exist].

(55) His (Ptah's) Ennead is before him as teeth and lips, [they are] as the semen and hands of Atum, for [it is said that] the Ennead of Atum came into being by means of his semen and his fingers. But the Ennead [of Ptah] is the teeth and lips in this mouth which pronounced the name of everything, from which Shu and Tefnut came forth, (56) and which gave birth to the Ennead.

The sight of the eyes, the hearing of the ears, the breathing of the nose, they report to the heart, and it (the heart) causes every understanding (i.e. completed concept) to come forth, and it is the tongue which repeats what the heart has thought out (i.e. devised). Thus all gods were born and his (Ptah's) Ennead was completed. For every word of the god came into being by means of what the heart thought out and the tongue commanded.

(57) So were made all the kas, and the hemsut were determined, [i.e.] those [spirits or faculties and qualities] which make all foods and provisions, by means of this word [which the heart thought out and which came forth on the tongue]. [Thus justice is done] to him who does what is liked [and punishment to] him who does what is disliked. Thus life is given to him who has peace (i.e. is peaceful and law-abiding) and death to him who has sin (i.e. who is a criminal). Thus were made all works and all crafts, the action of the hands and the movement of the legs, (58) and the activity of every member, in accordance with the command which is thought out by the heart and comes forth on the tongue and creates the performance of everything.[3]

And so is said of Ptah [this epithet]: "He who made all and brought the gods into being." He is Tatenen, who gave birth to the gods and from whom every thing came forth: food, provisions, offerings for the gods, and all good things. So it was discovered and understood that he is the mightiest of the gods. And so Ptah was satisfied after he had made everything and all the divine words.

He gave birth to the gods,
He made the towns,
He founded the nomes,
He put the gods into their (60) shrines.
He settled their offerings,
He founded their shrines,
He made their bodies (i.e. their statues) as they desired [them].

So the gods entered into their bodies,
Of every wood, every stone, every clay,
And of every thing which grows upon him [as Tatenen]
(61) In which their forms resided.
Thus all gods were gathered in him, and also their kas,
Content and united with the Lord of the Two Lands.

# Notes to Document II.9

1.  This first line contains the full five-fold titulary of King Shabaka. The special relationship with Ptah that is stressed in the second line is immediately suggested after the titulary in line 1. In both lines Ptah is given the very old epithet South of his Wall. In the second line he is also called Ptah-Tatenen, which name is probably of New-Kingdom origin.

2.  Following the suggestions of Sethe and Junker, Miss Lichtheim, *Ancient Egyptian Literature*, Vol. 1, p. 54, gives the following alternative translations of this paragraph: "(53) There took shape in the heart, there took shape on the tongue the form of Atum. For the very great one is Ptah, who gave [life] to all the gods and their *kas* through this heart and through this tongue, (54) in which Horus had taken shape as Ptah, in which Thoth had taken shape as Ptah. [Alternative reading: (53) Heart took shape in the form of Atum, Tongue took shape in the form of Atum. It is Ptah, the very great, who has given [[life]] to all the gods and their *kas* through this heart and through this tongue, (54) from which Horus had come forth as Ptah, from which Thoth had come forth as Ptah."]

3.  For the translation of this last clause, see Lichtheim, *Ancient Egyptian Literature*, Vol. 1, pp. 55 and 57, n. 13.

# Document II.10: Introduction

## A Dream-Book

This work appears on the recto of a papyrus of the nineteenth dynasty (British Museum, Papyrus Chester Beatty III=10683) and is written in Middle Egyptian "with hardly a trace of the Late-Egyptian Idiom, either in vocabulary or grammar."[1] Gardiner believes that[2]

it is, indeed, the earliest Dream-book in existence and may well date back to the Twelfth Dynasty ..., though this cannot be proved with certainty. The core of the work consists of a long enumeration of dreams in clear tabular form, accompanied by their interpretations. A vertical column of large hieratic signs occupies the entire height of the page, and yields the sense *If a man see himself in a dream .....*. This clause has to be read before each separate horizontal line to the left of the column, only one horizontal line being allowed for each dream. The descriptions of the dreams are necessarily very terse, and are divided off from the interpreter's equally terse judgment upon them by a small space. The general scheme is thus as follows: '*If a man see himself in a dream [doing-so-and-so], good* (or *bad*); it means such-and-such a thing will happen.' .... From twenty-five to twenty-eight dreams go to the page, after which the scribe starts afresh from the top with a new vertical column. The good dreams form a solid block, like the less numerous bad dreams that follow. The word '*bad*', being a word of ill omen, is written in red [represented by caps in Doc. II.10 below], the colour of blood .... It seems legitimate to suppose that the work opened with some such general title as '*The book of the interpretation of dreams*', to which may even have been appended the name of the reputed author .... Such a beginning of the book [in which good Horian dreams are distinguished from bad Sethian ones], if ever it existed, is completely lost, and in the first preserved page we find ourselves in the midst of the good Horian dreams.

I have already suggested in Chapter Two above that the gods were often considered to be the source of dreams, but that a god did not directly communicate with ordinary people as he occasionally did with the king. It is perhaps because of the divine origin of dreams that the message of the dream is only indirectly indicated. Indeed the interpretation of the dream rests on using words that are either identical or similar to those in which the action of the dream is expressed. In the latter case it is clear that the similarity is in the sounds of the words and so rests on punning. The reader will recall how popular punning was with the creator god (whoever he was) when he created by asserting the names of the entities he had conceived in his heart. Something like this process was evident when the god introduced the dream into the dreamer, and I have followed Gardiner in noting in parentheses some of the identities or similarities in the key words of dream and interpretation. But other relationships between dream and interpretation are also evident in this dream-book, as Gardiner points out:[3]

> Between dream and interpretation there was necessarily a certain correspondence of idea, and it was this correspondence which enabled the interpreter to declare the former portended the latter. Often the resemblance was restricted simply to the occurrence of the same word in the verbal descriptions .... Elsewhere the correspondence is more symbolical. For example, to see one's face in a mirror is to discover a second self, which second self must naturally have a wife; hence the interpretation *it means another wife* (7,11). Again to dream you are bringing in the cattle means that your people will be assembled to you ..., or if you see a large cat this signifies that your harvest will be a

big one (4,3) .... A rarer form of correspondence is that manifesting itself in contraries. Thus to see oneself dead is to have long life in prospect (4,13) .... Beyond the dichotomy of good and bad dreams, no attempt at classification is visible .... A point of special interest is the frequent reference to a man's dependence upon *his god*, which probably refers, not to the good god (Horus) or the bad god (Seth) represented by the man himself, but rather to the 'city-god'... so often mentioned in the texts of the Middle Kingdom.

No separate bibliographical section is necessary for this document, since I am wholly dependent on A. H. Gardiner, *Hieratic Papyri in the British Museum. Third Series. Chester Beatty Gift*, 2 vols. (London, 1935); see Vol. 1, pp. 9-23, and Vol. 2, plates 5-8. I have simply used the Gardiner translation in Vol. 1 and referred to the text in the plates of Vol. 2. I have changed Gardiner's formatting somewhat in order to accommodate it to my computerized printing program.

# Notes to the Introduction of Document II.10

1.   Gardiner, *Hieratic Papyri .... Third Series. Chester Beatty Gift*, Vol. 1, p. 10.
2.   *Ibid.*, pp. 9-10.
3.   *Ibid.*, pp. 21-22.

# Document II.10

## A Dream-Book

[IF A MAN SEE HIMSELF IN A DREAM]
..... ---- [good]
..... ---- [good]
     (The number of dreams lost is unknown)
(1,13) .... ---- good; it means putting .... in his hand.
     (I skip the rest of the lines on this page, the dreams being lost, though the interpretations are for the most part complete.)
(2,1) with his mouth split open *(sd)*, ---- good; it means something he was afraid of will be opened up *(sd)* by the god.
     (skipping one line)
(2,3) .... a crane *(d̠ʲt)*, ---- good; it means prosperity *(wd̠ʲ)*.
     (skipping two lines)
(2,6) munching lotus leaves (?), ---- [good]; it means something he will enjoy.
(2,7) shooting at a mark, ---- [good]; it means something good will happen to him.
     (skipping several lines)
(2,11) his penis becoming large, ---- [good]; it means his possessions will multiply.
     (skipping two lines)
(2,14) seeing the god who is above, ---- good; it means much food.
     (skipping a number of lines)

(2,23) up a growing tree *(nht)*, ----    good; it means his loss *(nhy)* of ....

(2,24) looking out a window, ---- good; it means the hearing of his cry by his god.

(2,25) rushes being given to him, ---- good; it means the hearing of his cry.

(2,26) seeing himself on a roof, ---- good; it means finding something.

(skipping two lines)

(3,2) seeing himself [in] mourning, ---- good; the increase of his possessions.

(skipping a line)

(3,4) white *(ḥḏ)* bread being given to him, ---- good; it means something given to him, at which his face will brighten up *(ḥḏ)*.

(3,5) drinking wine, ---- good; it means living in righteousness.

(skipping a line)

(3,7) copulating with his mother..., ---- good; [his?] clansmen will cleave fast to him.

(3,8) copulating with his sister, ---- good; it means the bequeathing of something to him.

(skipping a number of lines)

(4,3) seeing a large cat *(my ᶜ³)*, ---- good; it means a large harvest *(šmw ᶜ³)* will come to [him].

(skipping three lines)

(4,7) seeing himself upon a tree, ---- good; the destruction of all his ills.

(4,8) killing an ox, ---- good; killing his enemies.

(skipping two lines)

(4,11) climbing up a mast, ---- good; his being suspended aloft by his god.

(4,12) destroying his clothes, ---- good; his release from all ills.

(4,13) seeing himself dead, ----good; a long life [in] front of him.

(skipping a number of lines)

(4,22) being given victuals *(ᶜnḫw)* belonging to a temple, ---- good; the bestowing of life *(ᶜnḫ)* upon him by his god.

(4,23) sailing in a boat, ----good; it means sitting among his [distant] townsfolk.

(skipping a number of lines)

(5,9) reading aloud from a papyrus, ---- good; the establishment of a man in his house.

(skipping a number of lines)

(5,22) [seeing] the moon shining, ---- good; the pardoning of him by his god.

(skipping a number of lines)

(6,21) praising [Re?], ---- good; his being found innocent before his god.

(skipping two lines)

(6,24) seeing Bedouins, ---- good; the love of his father when he dies will come into his presence.

(skipping three lines)

(7,3) copulating with a female jerboa, ---- BAD; the passing of a judgment against him.

(7,4) drinking warm beer, ---- BAD; it means suffering will come upon him.

(7,5) eating ox-flesh, ---- good; it means something will accrue to him.

(skipping four lines)

(7,10) removing one of his legs, ---- BAD; judgment upon him(?) by those yonder [i.e. the dead].

(7,11) seeing his face in a mirror, ---- BAD; it means another wife.

(7,12) the god making his tears for him ---- BAD; it means fighting.

(skipping one line)

(7,14) eating hot meat, ---- BAD; it means his not being found innocent.

(skipping two lines)

(7,17) copulating with a woman,---- BAD; it means mourning.

(7,18) being bitten by a dog, ---- BAD; a cleaving fast to him of magic.

(7,19) being bitten by a snake, ---- BAD; it means the arising of words with him.

(7,20) measuring barley, ---- BAD; it means the arising of words with him.

(7,21) writing on a papyrus, ---- BAD; the reckoning up of his misdeeds by his god.

(skipping one line)

(7,23) having a spell put upon his mouth by another (?), ---- BAD; it means mourning.

(skipping a number of lines)

(8,2) seeing his penis stiff *(nḫtw)*, ---- BAD; victory to *(nḫtw)* his enemies.

(skipping two lines)

(8,5) looking into a deep well, ---- BAD; his being put in prison.

(skipping three lines)

(8,9) folding wings around himself(?), ---- BAD; he will not be found innocent with his god.

(8,10) copulating with a kite, ---- BAD; it means robbing him of something.

(skipping two lines)

(8,13) seeing a dwarf, --- BAD; the taking away of half of his life.

(8,14) falling a prey to (?) the council ---- BAD; his being driven from his office.

(skipping two lines)

(8,17) shaving his lower parts,---- BAD; it means mourning.

(skipping a number of lines)

(9,2) being made into an official, ---- BAD; death is close at hand.

(9,3) an Asiatic garment upon him, ---- BAD; his removal from his office.

(9,4) seeing people afar off, ---- BAD; his death is at hand.

(skipping three lines)

(9,8) seeing the heavens raining, --- BAD; words have come up against him.

(skipping one line)

(9,10) uncovering his own backside (pḥwy), ----BAD; he will be an orphan later (ḥr pḥwy).

(9,11) eating figs and grapes, ----BAD; it means illness.

(skipping two lines)

(9,14) putting his face to the ground, ---- BAD; the requirement of something from him by those yonder (i.e. the dead).

(9,15) seeing a burning fire, ---- BAD; the removal of his son or his brother.

(9,16) copulating with a pig, ---- BAD; being deprived of his possessions.

(skipping one line)

(9,18) drinking blood, ---- BAD; a fight awaits him.

(skipping three lines)

(9,22) copulating with his wife in daylight, ---- BAD; the seeing of his misdeeds by his god.

(skipping three lines)

(9,26) seizing wood belonging to the god in his hand, ---- BAD; finding misdeeds in him by his god.

(9,27) looking after monkeys, ---- BAD; a change awaits him.

(9,28) fetching mice from the field, ---- BAD; a sore heart.
(10,1) sailing downstream, ---- BAD; violent words.
        (skipping six lines)
(10,8) putting beer into a vessel, ---- BAD; the removal of something from his house.
(10,9) breaking a vessel with his feet, ---- BAD; it means fighting.

[Incantation to Isis][1]

(10,10) To be recited by a man when he wakes in his [own] place. 'Come to me, come to me, my mother Isis. Behold I am seeing what is (?) far from me in my (?) city.' 'Here am I, my son Horus, come out with what thou hast seen, in order that my afflictions(?) throughout thy dreams may vanish, and fire go forth against him that frighteneth thee. Behold, I am come that I may see thee and drive forth thy ills and extirpate all that is filthy.' 'Hail to thee, thou (?) good dream which art seen [by] night (10,15) or by day. Driven forth are all evil filthy things which Seth, the son of Nut, has made. [Even as] Re is vindicated against his enemies, [so] I am vindicated against my enemies.'
        This spell is to be spoken by a man when he wakes in his [own] place, there having been given to him *pesen*-bread in [his] presence and some fresh herbs moistened with beer and myrrh. A man's face is to be rubbed therewith, and all evil dreams that [he] has seen are driven away.

# Note to Document II.10

1.    Gardiner, *Hieratic Papyri ... Third Series.*

*Chester Beatty Gift*, Vol. 1, p. 19: "At this point the catalogue of dreams gives place to an incantation for the protection of the dreamer, and here for the first time we receive a hint that Horus was regarded as the prototype of the normal Egyptian man whose nocturnal visions were interpreted in the first half of the book. The text of the spells is unhappily rather corrupt, though not to the extent of rendering it wholly unintelligible. The form of a dialogue is adopted, Horus calling upon his mother Isis to shield him from the baneful consequences portended by his dreams. These consequences are of course ascribed to the machinations of Seth."

# Document II.11: Introduction

## The Harris Magical Papyrus

The papyrus which is known as the Harris Magical Papyrus is Harris Papyrus 501 (=British Museum Papyrus 10042). It was purchased by the British Consul-General Mr. A.C. Harris in Alexandria in 1855. At that time it was complete and was almost nine feet in length.[1] This was its condition when tracings were made from it by Chabas for his edition of it in 1860 (see the bibliographical paragraph below).[2] But by the time it was purchased from Mr. Harris's daughter by the British Museum in 1872, it was in a seriously mutilated state as the result of a powder explosion in Alexandria, and the two remaining portions together are but five feet in length. Hence the tracings of Chabas played an important role in the best hieroglyphic text and study of the papyrus produced by H.O. Lange in 1927. The recto of the papyrus is in a book-hand of the nineteenth or twentieth dynasty, i.e., it is a Ramesside document. The verso is in a careless hand not much later than that of the recto.[3]

The varied content of hymns and magical spells (primarily against the crocodile) has been neatly described by Lange,[4] and I confine myself to noting that the parts of interest for cosmogony (which I have extracted as Document II.11) are primarily those which are hymns. Pieces B-D are three hymns to Shu (or three parts of a single hymn). Shu is called the heir of Re and his power is like that of Re himself as the Lord of Transformations. I have already mentioned that by the time of the *Coffin Texts* Shu was described as having an important auxiliary role in creation. Re has supplied his heir with magic (B,14-15). Shu's kas (his spiritual attributes) rest in Re's, the latter nourishing the former. In normal Egyptian fashion a will was drawn up in Hermopolis by Reharakhti's scribe, Thoth, who is called Lord of Hermopolis, the transfer of power being thereby "established, confirmed, and perpetuated in writing" (B,22). Shu is further described as "begotten of Atum himself, who has created himself, without there being a mother" (C,2-3). Shu is said to have brought the Eye of his father to him, rather reversing the usual story that Shu and Tefenet were lost in the Abyss and Atum accordingly sent his eye to fetch them. The hymn in D which celebrates the various attributes of Shu epitomized in his various names resembles the *Litany of Re* and shows once again what an important role Shu has assumed in this account.

In hymn E, Sepu, an epithet of Re as personifying the "First Time" of creation (?), is addressed as the one who made his own body, the One Lord who came out of the Abyss. He is called Hu, the self-creator who made the food in him, the one who created both his father and mother.

In hymn F the creator is also called "you Five Great Gods who came out of the City of Hermopolis," a title I have discussed in Chapter Two, and it is asserted that his own creation preceded his being in the heaven and on the earth and was before the sun first shone, a poetic description of the first stage of creation.

Hymn G to Amon-Re was quoted in Chapter Two above and its cosmogonic aspects need only brief mention here: the Hermopolitan influence which is evident in the insertion of the Ogdoad into the creation process (G,3), creation by the word (G,7), Amun's transformation of himself into "millions" (G,8), his limitless size (G,9), his early form as a serpent (G,11), and his richness of magic and secret forms (G,12).

The creator also takes on the name of Tatenen "who lifted himself up" (G,20), thus showing that Amun borrows from the traditions of Ptah at Memphis as well as from those of Re at Heliopolis and the Ogdoad at Hermopolis.

The influence of the Hermopolitan doctrines is also apparent in pieces H and K. In H the Ogdoad worship the god who is in their midst (H,2), the great god being described in the common fashion as having bones of silver, flesh of gold, and hair of real lapis lazuli (H,3-4).[5] The Ogdoad speak of Amun's hiding himself in his pupil, i.e. in his sun disk (H,6-7), as "wondrous of forms" and as the "sacred one whom nobody knows" (H,8). In K the god is called in Hermopolitan terms the Egg of the water, the Seed of the earth, and the Essence (?) of the Ogdoad of Hermopolis (K,5-6). There is also reference to the Lake of the Two Knives, apparently located in Hermopolis. The hymn in K shows the not uncommon union of Amun and Min (K,11-12). The theme of the primordial egg is continued in the final assertion that the spell is "to be recited over the egg of the navel" held in his hand by a person in the bow of a ship (K,13-14).

My final extract from the Harris Magical Papyrus celebrates the creator as the "Image of millions of millions" and the "single Khnum of his son" (M,2-3). This is a poetic reference to Khnum's creating activity on his potter's wheel and thus means simply that by himself the creator god has fashioned or crafted his son. A final reference to the doctrine of the Great Cackler, honking in the primordial night, is worth noting (M,9).

### Texts and Studies of the Harris Magical Papyrus

As I have indicated above, the first text of the papyrus was produced through tracings made by F. Chabas, *Le Papyrus Magique Harris* (Chalons-sur-Saône, 1860). This work included a translation and commentary and was a remarkable work considering the knowledge of hieratic writing at this time. Chabas made another translation later: Chabas, *Mélanges égyptologiques*, 3rd Series, Vol. 2 (Chalons-sur-Saône and Paris, 1873), pp. 242-78.

E.A.W. Budge published facsimiles of the text (along with Chabas's tracings of the then lost pages): *Facsimiles of Egyptian Hieratic Papyri in the British Museum, With Descriptions, Translations, etc.* (London, 1910), plates 20-30. This work also included the first hieroglyphic transcription (separate pag., pp. 34-40) and a now greatly out-of-date translation (separate pag., pp. 23-27).

The next step (with no great progress in understanding the text) was taken by E. Akmar, who published a hieroglyphic transcription of the text along with a French translation: *Le Papyrus Magique Harris transcrit et publié* (Upsala, 1916).

French extracts were published by F. Lexa, *La magie dans l'Égypte antique de l'Ancien Empire jusqu'à l'Époque Copte*, Vol. 2 (Paris, 1925), pp. 35-44.

By far the most important work on this papyrus was that of H.O. Lange, *Der magische Papyrus Harris* (Copenhagen, 1927), which includes a new hieroglyphic transcription, a fine German translation, and an extensive commentary. It is this work on which I have depended almost exclusively in making my translation. I have used Lange's letters to distinguish the various pieces that make up the text.

# Notes to the Introduction of Document II.11

1. Budge, *Facsimiles of Hieratic Papyri*, p. xv.
2. Lange, *Der magische Papyrus Harris*, p. 6.
3. *Ibid.*, p. 7.
4. *Ibid.*, pp. 8-11.
5. See above, Document II.6, (2), note 1.

# Document II.11

## The Harris Magical Papyrus

### A.
The Beautiful Spells for Singing
Which Drive Away the Swimming One (i.e. the
Crocodile)

### B.
Hail to you, Heir of Re,
Eldest son, who comes forth from his body,
The one whom he selected before all of his children,
Whose power is like that of the Lord of
Transformations,
(5) Who kills the enemies every day.
When the ship [of the sun] has a good wind, your heart
is pleased;
The morning bark is in jubilee,
When they [in the bark] see Shu, the son of Re,
vindicated,
When he has put his spear into the serpent villain.
(10) When Re travels the sky each morning,
Then Tefenet rests upon his head
And hurls her flame against his enemies,
So that they (corr. from he) are made as ones
nonexistent.
You whom Re has amply provided with a divinity of
magic,
(15) As an heir upon the throne of his father,

Whose kas rest in the kas of Re
As food for the nourishment of that which is near him,
[You] for whom he has made a will,
Written out by the Lord of Hermopolis [i.e. Thoth],
(20) The ... scribe of Reharakhti,
In the palace of the Great Double House of Heliopolis;
It is established, confirmed, and perpetuated in writing,
Under the feet of Reharakhti,
And he shall transmit it to the son of his son for ever
and ever.

## C.

Hail to you, you son of Re,
Begotten of Atum himself,
Who has created himself, without there being a mother,
The True One, the Lord of the Double Truth,
(5)You Powerful One, who has power over the gods,
Who brings the Eye of his father Re,
To whom they bring gifts in their own hands,
....

## D.

You are mysterious, you are greater than the [other]
gods
In your name of Shu, son of Re.
....

(5) You are greater and richer than the [other] gods
In your name of The Very Great Divine One.
.... [and there follows a series of attributes of Shu
reflected in special names.]

## E.

O Sepu (i.e. One of the First Time?), who made his own
body.

O One Lord, who came out of the Abyss.
O Hu, who created himself.
O One who made this food which is in him.
(5) O One who has created his father and borne his mother.

### F.

Hail to you, you Five Great Gods
Who came out of the City of Eight (Hermopolis),
You who were not yet in heaven (i.e., who existed before the heaven).
You who were not yet upon the earth (i.e., who existed before the earth),
(5) You who were not yet illumined by the sun (i.e., who existed before the sun shone).
....

### G.

Adoration of Amon-Reharakhti, who came into being by himself,
Who founded the land when he began [to create],
Made by the Ogdoad of Hermopolis (or Who made the Ogdoad of Hermopolis) in the first primordial time.
....
(5) Amun the primordial god of the Two Lands
When he arose from Nun and Nunet.
What was said [came into being] on the water and on the land.
Hail to you, the One who made himself into millions,
Whose length and breadth are without limit,
(10) Ready Power who bore himself,
The primordial serpent who is powerful of flame,
The One rich in magic with secret forms,
....

(20) Tatenen who lifted himself up (*or* extolled himself)
over the gods,
The Elder one who rejuvenates himself and lives
through eternity *(nḥḥ)*,
Amun who is established in every thing,
This god who brought forth the earth by means of his
plans,
Come to me, O Lord of the Gods, L.P.H.
....

### H.

To be said by the Ogdoad of the primordial company of
gods,
Great ones, who worship the god who is in their midst,
His bones are of silver and his flesh of gold,
His hair of real lapis lazuli.
(5) The Ogdoad says:
O Amun, who hides himself in the pupil [of] his [eye],
Soul who shines in his sound eye *(wḏ't)*,
One wondrous of forms, sacred one whom nobody
knows,
Who radiates his forms to make himself seen by means
of his brilliance,
(10) One mysterious of mysteries, whose secrets are not
known,
Praise to you up to the body of Nut (i.e. to heaven)!
Righteous are your children, the gods;
Maat is joined with your secret chapel,
....

### K.

....

(5) O you Egg of the water, Seed of the earth,
... (Essence?) of the Ogdoad of Hermopolis,

Great One in the Heaven and Great One in the Netherworld,
Residing in the nest in front of the Lake of the Two Knives,
I have emerged with you from the water,
(10) I have left with you from your nest,
I am Min of Gebtu (Koptos=Qift),
I am Min, Lord of the Land of Gebtu,
This spell will be recited over the egg of the navel,
Which is placed in the hand of a person in the bow of a ship.
....

## M.

Another spell:
Come to me, Come to me, O Image of millions of millions,
The single Khnum of his son (i.e. unique parent of his son),
The One who was conceived yesterday and born today,
(5) The One whose name I knew,
The One who has seventy-seven [pairs of] eyes,
And seventy-seven [pairs of] ears,
Come to me that you may hear my voice,
As the voice of the Great Cackler was heard in the Night.
(10) I am the Great Flooded-one, the Great Flooded-one.
To be recited four times.
..........

# Section Three

# Appendixes

# Chronology

In preparing the following chronology I have primarily used J. Baines and J. Málek, *Atlas of Ancient Egypt* (Oxford, 1980), pp. 36-37, and O. Neugebauer and R. A. Parker, *Egyptian Astronomical Texts*, Vol. 1 (Providence, Rhode Island, and London, 1960), p. 129. The latter I have consulted for the general dates of the periods and the dynasties through the First Intermediate Period, i.e. during the third millennium. The dates given by Baines and Málek for the periods and the individual monarchs of that millennium are reported in the footnotes. The names of monarchs and their order for the first five dynasties are those which I adopted in Chapter One above. Use has also been made of Parker's detailed chronology published in *The Encyclopedia Americana*, Vol. 10, article "Egypt". From the Middle Kingdom through the Greco-Roman Period, the main source of the dates is the work of Baines and Málek. For Dynasties 21-26 I have also referred to K. A. Kitchen, *The Third Intermediate Period in Egypt (1100-650 B.C.)* (Warminster, 1973, with Supplement, 1986). Except where indicated by asterisks, there is still considerable uncertainty about precise dates, though in most cases the divergencies of dating from the Middle Kingdom onward are small. Some of the problems arising in efforts to achieve precise dating will be discussed in Chapter Three in the next volume. The names of monarchs are given in the forms often used in this volume, i.e. with vowels supplied but with only common abbreviated phonetic renderings. Overlapping dates indicate joint or collateral regencies.

The reader may wish to consult the detailed chronology developed by A. H. Gardiner, *Egypt of the Pharaohs* (Oxford, 1961), pp. 429-33, since it correlates the names of the kings found in Manetho, the king-lists, and the monuments.

## EARLY DYNASTIC PERIOD: 3110-2665 B.C.[1]

*Dynasty 1:* Menes (Narmer?), Aha (sometimes thought to be Menes, as I have noted in Chapter One above), Djer, Djet or Wadji, Den, Adjib, Semerkhet, and Ka$^c$a.[2]

*Dynasty 2:* Hetepsekhemuy, Nebre, Ninetjer, Sekhemib, Peribsen (these last two kings are sometimes thought to be the same king; sometimes a King Weneg and King Sened are placed before Peribsen), Sened, Neferka, Neferkaseker, Khasekhem, and Khasekhemuy (the last two names may designate one king who changed his name; see Doc. I.1, n. 64).[3]

## OLD KINGDOM: 2664-2155.[4]

*Dynasty 3:* 2664-2615: Zanakht (=Nebka?), Djoser (Netjeri-khet), Sekhemkhet (Djoser-tety), Khaba, and Huny.[5]

*Dynasty 4:* 2614-2502: Sneferu, Khufu (Cheops), Djedefre or Redjedef, Rekhaef (Chephren) (sometimes a king Baufre is added here), Menkaure (Mycerinus), and Shepseskaf.[6]

*Dynasty 5:* 2501-2342: Weserkaf, Sahure, Neferirkare Kakai, Shepseskare Ini, Reneferef, Niuserre Izi, Menkauhor, Djedkare Izezi or Issy, and Wenis or Unis.[7]

*Dynasty 6:* 2341-2181: Teti, Pepy I (Meryre), Merenre Nemtyemzaf, and Pepy II (Neferkare).[8]

*Dynasties 7 and 8:* Interregnum and 2174-2155: As Baines and Málek note, there are numerous ephemeral kings assigned to these dynasties, and they date these dynasties 2150-2134.

## FIRST INTERMEDIATE PERIOD: 2154-2052
(Neugebauer and Parker) or 2134-2040 (Baines and Málek). From this point on I quote in the main chronology the dates of the dynasties and of their kings given by Baines and Málek, preserving however the spelling of the kings' names that I have adopted throughout this and the succeeding volumes.

*Dynasties 9 and 10:* These are the Heracleopolitan dynasties with several kings called Khety; Merykare; and Ity. In Thebes during this same period several princes ruled locally, the last of whom, Nebhepetre (Mentuhotep), conquered the Heracleopolitans and assumed the kingship as the first Theban king of all Egypt in the eleventh dynasty.

## MIDDLE KINGDOM: 2040-1640
*Dynasty 11:* 2040-1991: Nebhepetre Mentuhotep 2061-2010, Sankhare Mentuhotep 2010-1998, Nebtawyre Mentuhotep 1998-1991.

*Dynasty 12:* *1991-1783: Sehetepibre Amenemhet I *1991-1962, Kheperkare Senwosret or Senusert (Sesostris) I *1971-1926, Nubkaure Amenemhet II *1929-1892, Khakeperre Senwosret II *1897-1878, Khakaure Senwosret III *1878-1841?, Nimaatre Amenemhet III 1844-1797, Maakkerure Amenemhet IV 1799-1787, Sebekkaure Nefrusobk 1787-1783.

*Dynasty 13:* 1783-after 1640. About 70 kings. Some of the more important monarchs are given by Baines and Málek. See also Gardiner, *Egypt of the*

*Pharaohs*, pp. 440-41. The fourteenth dynasty (at Xois?) included a number of minor kings probably contemporary with the kings of Dynasty 13 or Dynasty 15.

## SECOND INTERMEDIATE PERIOD: 1640-1532

*Dynasty 15:* This was a Hyksos dynasty at Avaris and included Kings Salitis, Seshi, Khian, Apohis c. 1585-1542, and Khamudi c. 1542-1532.

*Dynasty 16:* Minor Hyksos kings or vassals contemporary with those of Dynasty 15.

*Dynasty 17:* 1640-1550: A number of Theban kings, the last two being Seqenenre Tao (or Djehutio) and Wadjikheperre Kamose c. 1555-1550.

## NEW KINGDOM: 1550-1070

*Dynasty 18:* 1550-1307: Nebpehtire Ahmose 1550-1525, Djeserkare Amenhotep (Amenophis) I 1525-1504, Akheperkare Tuthmosis I 1504-1492, Akheperenre Tuthmosis II 1492-1479, Menkheperre Tuthmosis III 1479-1425, Maatkare Hatshepsut (the pharaoh queen) 1473-1458 who ruled with Tuthmosis III in the background until he took over the sole rule, Akheprure Amenhotep II 1427-1401, Menkheprure Tuthmosis IV 1401-1391, Nebmaatre Amenhotep III 1391-1353, Neferkheprure waenre Amenhotep IV (=Akhenaten) 1353-1335, Ankhkeprure Smenkhkare 1335-1333, Nebkheprure Tutankhamun 1333-1323, Kheperkheprure Ay (or Aya) 1323-1319, Djeserkheprure Haremhab 1319-1307.

*Dynasty 19:* 1307-1196: Menpehtire Ramesses I 1307-1306, Menmaatre Seti or Sety (Sethos) I 1306-1290, Usermaatre setepenre Ramesses II 1290-1224, Baenre hotephirmaat Merneptah or Merenptah 1224-1214,

Userkheprure setepenre Seti II 1214-1204, Menmire Amenmesse, a usurper in the reign of Seti II, Akhenre setepenre Siptah 1204-1198, Sitre meritamun Twosre or Tausert, a queen, 1198-1196.

*Dynasty 20:* 1196-1070: Userkhaure meryamun Sethnakhte 1196-1194, Usermaatre meryamun Ramesses III 1194-1163, Heqamaatre setepenamun Ramesses IV 1163-1156, Usermaatre sekheperenre Ramesses V 1156-1151, Nebmaatre meryamun Ramesses VI 1151-1143, Usermaatre setepenre Ramesses VII 1143-1136, Usermaatre akhenamun Ramesses VIII 1136-1141, Neferkare setepenre Ramesses IX 1131-1112, Khepermaatre setepenre Ramesses X 1112-1100, Menmaatre setepenptah Ramesses XI 1100-1070.

## THIRD INTERMEDIATE PERIOD:[9] 1070-712

*Dynasty 21:* 1070-945: Hedjkheperre setepenre Smendes 1070-1044,[10] Neferkare Amenemnisu 1044-1040,[11] Akheperre setepenamun Pausennes I 1040-992,[12] Usermaatre setepenamun Amenemope 993-984, Akheperre setepenre Osorkon[13] I 984-978, Netjerkheperre setepenamun Siamun 978-959, Titkheprure setepenre Pausennes II 959-945.

*Dynasty 22:* 945-712: Hedjkheperre setepenre Shoshenq I 945-924, Sekhemkheperre setepenre Osorkon II 924-909, Usermaatre setepenamum Takelot I 909-, Heqakheperre setepenre Shoshenq II -883, Usermaatre setepenamun Osorkon III 883-855, Hedjkheperre setepenre Takelot II 860-835, Usermaatre setepenre Shoshenq III 835-781, Usermaatre setepenre/amun Pami 783-773, Akheperre Shoshenq V 773-735, Akheperre setepenamun Osorkon V 735-712.[14]

*Dynasty 23:* c. 828-712: Baines and Málek remark concerning this dynasty: "Various contemporary lines of kings recognized in Thebes, Hermopolis, Herakleopolis, Leontopolis and Tanis; precise arrangement and order are still disputed." Pedubaste I 828-803, Osorkon IV 777-749, Neferkare Peftjauawybast 740-725.[15]

*Dynasty 24:* 724-712 at Sais: (Shepsesre? Tefnakhte 724-717), Wahkare Bocchoris 717-712.[16]

*Dynasty 25:* 770-712 (Nubia and Theban area): Nimaatre Kashta 770-750, Usermaatre (and other names) Piye 750-712.

### LATE PERIOD: 712-332

*Dynasty 25:* 712-657 (Nubia and all Egypt): Neferkare Shabaka 712-698, Djedkaure Shebitku 698-690, Khure nefertem Taharqa 690-664, Bakare Tantamani 664-657 (possibly later in Nubia).[17]

*Dynasty 26* (Saite): *664-525: (Necho I *672-664), Wahibre Psammetichus I *664-610, Wehemibre Necho II *610-595, Neferibre Psammetichus II *595-589, Haaibre Apries *589-570, Khnemibre Amasis *570-526, Ankhkaenre Psammetichus III *526-525.

*Dynasty 27* (Persian): *525-404: Cambyses *525-522, Darius I *521-486, Xerxes I *486-466, Artaxerxes I *465-424, Darius II *424-404.

*Dynasty 28:* Amyrtaios *404-399.

*Dynasty 29:* *399-380 Baenre merynetjeru Nepherites I *399-393, Userre setepenptah Psammuthis *393, Khnemmaatre Hakoris *393-380, Nepherites II *380.

*Dynasty 30:* *380-343: Kheperkare Nectanebo I *380-362, Irmaatenre Teos *365-360, Senedjemibre setepenanhur Nectanebo II *360-343.

*2nd Persian Period (sometimes called Dynasty 31):* *343-332: Artaxerxes III Ochus *343-338, Arses *338-336, Darius III Codoman *335-332. Period interrupted by a native ruler Senetanen setepenptah Khababash.

## GRECO-ROMAN PERIOD: *332 B.C.-395 A.D.

*Macedonian Dynasty:* *332-304: Alexander III the Great *332-323, Philip Arrhidaeus *323-316. Alexander IV *316-304.

*Ptolemaic Dynasty:* *304-30: Ptolemy I *304-284, Ptolemy II *285-246, Ptolemy III *246-221, Ptolemy IV *221-205, Ptolemy V *205-180, Ptolemy VI *180-164, *163-145, Ptolemy VIII *170-163, *145-116, Ptolemy VII *145, Cleopatra III and Ptolemy IX *116-107, Cleopatra III and Ptolemy X *107-88, Ptolemy IX *88-81, Cleopatra Berenice *81-80, Ptolemy XI *80, Ptolemy XII *80-58, *55-51, Berenice IV *58-55, Cleopatra VII *51-30, Ptolemy XIII *51-47, Ptolemy XIV *47-44, Ptolemy XV Caesarion *44-30.

*Roman Emperors down to the last use of hieroglyphics:* *30 B.C.-395 A.D.: I mention only the first two, Augustus *30 B.C.-14 A.D. and Tiberius *14-37, and the twelfth, Trajan *98-117.

# Notes to the Chronology

1.    Baines and Málek have a preceding period entitled Late Predynastic, in which they include Kings Zekhen and Narmer. This period they date as c. 3000. Presumably the Neugebauer-Parker chronology of the Early Dynastic Period would include Narmer as the first dynastic king, since Parker in his earlier chronology in the *Encyclopedia Americana* has the same dates as in his later chronology and the former does include Narmer as the first king. Also note that Baines and Málek insert the third dynasty as a part of the Early Dynastic Period, and they date that period as 2920-2575.

2.    Parker in his chronology in the *Encyclopedia Americana* dates the various kings of this dynasty as follows: Menes (Narmer), Ity (Hor-Aha), dated together as 3110-3056; Iteti (Djer) 3055-3009; Interregnum 3008; Iti? (Djet), Zemti (Udimu) (Den), the last two kings dated together 3007-2975; Merpabia (Adjib) 2974-2917; Iryneter (Semerkhet) 2917-2909); and Qaa (Qaa Sen) 2908-2884.

3.    Parker in his detailed chronology gives the following monarchs and their dates: Hetep (Hetepsekhemuy), Nubnefer (Reneb), these two kings are dated together 2883-2811; Nineter 2810-2766; Weneg 2766-2747; Sened 2747-2733; Peribsen 2733-2718; Neferkasokar 2718-2711; Khasekhem 2711-2691; and Khasekhemuy 2691-2665.

4.    Since Baines and Málek include the third dynasty with the Early Period, they date the Old Kingdom with the beginning of the fourth dynasty,

suggesting the span 2575-2134.

5.   Baines and Málek date the third dynasty between 2649 and 2575, with the individual reigns as follows: Zanakht 2649-2630, Djoser 2630-2611, Sekhemet 2611-2603, Khaba 2603-2599, and Huny 2599-2575. Parker in his detailed chronology gives the following kings and dates: Nebka (Sanakht) 2664, Djoser 2663-2645, Djoser Teti 2644-2639, and Huny 2638-2615.

6.   Baines and Málek date the fourth dynasty as 2575-2465, with the individual monarchs dated as follows: Sneferu (written as Snofru) 2575-2551, Khufu 2551-2528, Redjedef 2528-2520, Chephren 2520-2494, Menkaure 2490-2472, and Shepseskaf 2472-2467.

7.   Baines and Málek date the fifth dynasty 2465-2323, with the individual monarchs dated as follows: Weserkaf (written Userkaf) 2465-2458, Sahure 2458-2446, Neferirkare 2446-2426, Shepseskare 2426-2419, Reneferef 2419-2416, Niusserre (written Neussere) 2416-2392, Menkauhor 2396-2388, Djedkare Izezi 2388-2356, and Wenis 2356-2323.

8.   Baines and Málek date the sixth dynasty 2323-2150, with the individual monarchs dated as follows: Teti 2323-2291, Pepy I 2289-2255, Merenre 2255-2246, and Pepy II 2246-2152.

9.   Parker calls the period from Dynasty 21 through Dynasty 25 the Late Period, while Baines and Málek use that title for the time from Dynasty 25 through the second Persian period (=Dynasty 31). K. A. Kitchen uses the designation Third Intermediate Period as the title of his recent authoritative work, which I mentioned above in the introduction to this Chronology.

10.   Kitchen has 1069-1043. Kitchen also gives alternate dates for this and the following reigns (see p.

406 of his work).

11. Kitchen gives 1043-1039.

12. Kitchen gives 1039-991.

13. Parker writes Osokhor and Kitchen Osochor.

14. Parker has the following monarchs and dates for Dynasty 22: Sheshonk (Sheshonq) 940-919, Osorkon I 919-883, Takelot I 883-860, Osorkon II 860-833, Sheshonk II 837, Takelot II 837-823, Shesonk III 823-772, Pami 772-767, Sheshonk IV 767-730. Kitchen (p. 588) has the following monarchs and dates (I follow his renditions of the names of the kings): Shoshenq I 945-924, Osorkon I 924-889, Shoshenq II c. 890, Takeloth I 889-874, Osorkon II 874-850, Harsiese c. 870-860, Takeloth II 850-825, Shoshenq III 825-773, Pimay 773-767, Shoshenq V 767-730, Osorkon IV 730-715?/713?.

15. Parker has the following: Pedibast c. 761-738, Sheshonk V, Osorkon III, Takelot III, Amenrud, Osorkon IV, these last five dated c. 738-715. Kitchen (p. 588) has: Pedubast I 818-793, Input I 804-803?, Shoshenq IV 793-787, Osorkon III 787-759, Takeloth III 764-757, Rudamun 757-754, Input II 754-720 (or 715), (Shoshenq VI 720-715, existence doubtful).

16. Parker has: Tefnakht 725-715, Bocchoris 715-710. Kitchen (p. 589) has: Tefnakht I 727-720 (or less likely 727-719), Bakenranef 720-715 (or less likely 719-713).

17. Parker has no split of the dynasty but simply gives: (Ethiopian) Piankhi [=Piye] 736-?710, Shabaka (?) 710-696, Shabataka 698-685, Taharka 690-664, Tanutamon 664-657. Kitchen (p. 589) first gives a Proto-Saite Dynasty: Ammeris, Nubian governor?, 715-695, Stephinates, Tefnakht II?, 695-688, Nekauba 688-672, Menkheperre Necho I 672-664. He then

follows this dynasty with the twenty-fifth (Nubian) dynasty: Alara c. 780-760, Kashta c. 760-747, Piankhy 747-716, Shabako 716-702, Shebitku 702-690, Taharqa 690-664, Tantamani 664-656. Kitchen also presents a less likely set of dates for this dynasty.

# Abbreviations Used in Text and Bibliography

*ASAE* = *Annales du Service des Antiquités de l'Égypte.*

*BIFAO* = *Bulletin de l'Institut Français d'Archéologie Orientale.*

*JEA* = *The Journal of Egyptian Archaeology.*

*JNES* = *Journal of Near Eastern Studies.*

*MDAIK* = *Mitteilungen des Deutschen Archäologischen Instituts, Abteilung Kairo.*

*PSBA* = *Proceedings of the Society of Biblical Archaeology.*

*Urkunden* = G. Steindorff, ed., *Urkunden des ägyptischen Altertums* (For *Urkunden* I and IV, see the Bibliography, Sethe, K., *Urkunden des Alten Reichs* and *Urkunden der 18. Dynastie*. For *Urkunden* V, see Grapow, H., *Religiöse Urkunden*).

*Wb*, see the Bibliography, Erman, A., and H. Grapow, *Wörterbuch*.

*ZÄS* = *Zeitschrift für ägyptische Sprache und Altertumskunde.*

# Bibliography

Akmar, E., *Le Papyrus Magique Harris transcrit et publié* (Upsala, 1916).

Aldred, C., *Egypt to the End of the Old Kingdom* (London, 1965).

Aldred, C., *Egyptian Art in the Days of the Pharaohs* (New York and Toronto, 1980).

Allen, T.G., *Horus in the Pyramid Texts* (Chicago, 1916).

Allen, T.G., *The Book of the Dead or Going Forth by Day. Ideas of the Ancient Egyptians Concerning the Hereafter as Expressed in Their Own Terms (The Oriental Institute of the University of Chicago Studies in Ancient Oriental Civilization*, No. 37) (Chicago, 1974).

Allen, T.G., *The Egyptian Book of the Dead. Documents in the Oriental Institute Museum at the University of Chicago (The University of Chicago Oriental Institute Publications*, Vol. 82) (Chicago, 1969).

Altenmüller, H., "Hu," in W. Helck and W. Westendorf, eds. *Lexikon der Ägyptologie*, Vol. 3 (Wiesbaden, 1980), cc. 65-68.

Altenmüller, H., "Toten-Literatur. 22. Jenseitsbücher, Jenseitsführer," *Handbuch der Orientalistik*, Abt. 1, Vol. 1, Part 2 (Leiden, 1970), pp. 69-81.

Andrae, W., see Schäfer, H. and.

Andrews, C., see Faulkner, R.O., *The Ancient Egyptian Book of the Dead*.

Anthes, R., "Egyptian Theology in the Third Millennium B.C.," *JNES*, Vol. 18 (1959), pp. 169-212.

Anthes, R., "Mythology in Ancient Egypt," in S.N. Kramer, ed., *Mythologies of the Ancient World* (New York, 1961), pp. 1-92.

Anthes, R., "The Original Meaning of *m$^{)c}$ ḥrw*," *JNES*, Vol. 13 (1954), pp. 21-51.

Assmann, J., *Ägyptische Hymnen und Gebete* (Zurich and Munich, 1975).

Assmann, J., *Zeit und Ewigkeit im alten Ägypten* (Heidelberg, 1975).

Baedeker, K., *Egypt and the Sûdân* (Leipzig, 1929).

Baines, J. and J. Málek, *Atlas of Ancient Egypt*

(Oxford, 1980).

Barta, W., "Das Jahr in Datumsangaben und seine Bezeichnungen," *Festschrift Elmar Edel: 12 März 1979* (Bamberg, 1980), pp. 35-42.

Barta, W., "Die Chronologie der 1. bis 5. Dynastie nach den Angaben des rekonstruierten Annalenstein," *ZÄS*, Vol. 108 (1981), pp. 11-23.

Barucq, A., and F. Daumas, *Hymnes et prières de l'Égypte ancienne* (Paris, 1980).

Baumgartel, E.J., "Scorpion and Rosette and the Fragment of the Large Hierakonpolis Mace Head," *ZÄS*, Vol. 93 (1966), pp. 9-13.

Baumgartel, E.J., *The Cultures of Prehistoric Europe*, 2 vols. (London/New York/Toronto, 1955-60).

Bayoumi, A., *Autour du champ des souchets et du champ des offrandes* (Cairo, 1941).

Beckerath, J. von, "Die Lesung von 𓇳𓎟 'Regierungsjahr': Ein Vorschlag," *ZÄS*, Vol. 95, 2 (1969), pp. 88-91.

Beckerath, J. von, "*šmsj-Ḥrw* in der ägyptischen Vor- und Frühzeit," *MDAIK*, Vol. 14 (1956), pp. 1-10.

Beckerath, J. von, *Handbuch der ägyptischen Königsnamen* (Munich and Berlin, 1984), pp. 1-42.

Bell, B., "The Oldest Records of the Nile Floods," *The Geographical Journal*, Vol. 136 (1970), pp. 569-73.

Bissing, F.W. von, ed., *Das Re-Heiligtum des Königs Ne-Woser-Re*, Vol. 3: H. Kees, *Die grosse Festdarstellung* (Leipzig, 1928).

Bleeker, C.J., *Egyptian Festivals. Enactments of Religious Renewal* (Leiden, 1967).

Bonnet, H., *Reallexikon der ägyptischen Religionsgeschichte* (Berlin, 1952).

Borchardt, L., "Nilmesser und Nilstandsmarken," *Abhandlungen der Königlichen Preussischen Akademie der Wissenschaften*, 1906 (*Abhandlungen nicht zur Akademie gehöriger Gelehrter, Phil.-hist. Abh.*, I, pp. 1-55).

Borchardt, L., *Die Annalen und die zeitliche Festlegung des Alten Reiches der ägyptischen Geschichte* (Berlin, 1917).

Borchardt, L., *Denkmäler des alten Reiches (Ausser den Statuen) (Catalogue général des antiquités égyptiennes du Musée du Caire: Nos. 1295-1808)*, Part I (Berlin, 1937), Part II (Cairo, 1964).

Borchardt, L., *Das Grabdenkmal des Königs Sa'ḥu-Re^C*, Vol. 2 (Leipzig, 1913).

Borghouts, J.F., *Ancient Magical Texts* (Leiden, 1978).

Boylan, P., *Thoth: the Hermes of Egypt* (Oxford, 1922).

Breasted, J.H., "The Philosophy of a Memphite Priest," *ZÄS*, Vol. 39 (1901), pp. 39-54.

Breasted, J.H., "The Predynastic Union of Egypt," *BIFAO*, Vol. 30 (1931), pp. 709-14.

Breasted, J.H., *Ancient Records of Egypt*, 5 vols. (Chicago, 1906).

Breasted, J.H., *The Dawn of Conscience* (New York, 1933).

Breasted, J.H., *Development of Religion and Thought in Ancient Egypt* (New York, 1912; Harper Torchbook, 1959).

Breasted, J.H., *A History of Egypt*, 2nd ed. (New York, 1912).

Brugsch, H., "Bau und Maasse des Tempels von Edfu," *ZÄS*, Vol. 9 (1871), pp. 32-45.

Brugsch, H., *Religion und Mythologie der alten Ägypter* (Leipzig, 1891).

Brugsch, H., *Thesaurus inscriptionum*

*aegyptiacarum* (Leipzig, 1883-84; reprint, Graz, 1968).

Brunner, H., *Die Lehre des Cheti, Sohnes des Duauf (Ägyptologische Forschungen*, 13) (Glückstadt and Hamburg, 1944).

Brunner, H., *An Outline of Middle Egyptian Grammar for Use in Academic Instruction* (Graz, 1970).

Brunner-Traut, E., *Altägyptische Märchen* (Düsseldorf and Cologne, 1963).

Buck, A. de, *The Egyptian Coffin Texts*, 7 vols. (Chicago, 1935-61).

Buck, A. de, *Egyptian Reading Book*, Vol. 1 (Leiden, 1948).

Buck, A. de, *De Egyptische Voorstellingen betreffende den Oerheuvel* (Leiden, 1922).

Budge, E.A.W., *The Book of the Dead. An English Translation of the Chapters, Hymns, etc. of the Theban Recension*, 2nd ed., revised and enlarged, 3 vols. (London, 1909).

Budge, E.A.W., *The Chapters of Coming Forth by Day or the Theban Version of the Book of the Dead. The Egyptian Hieroglyphic Text Edited from Numerous Papyri*, 3 vols. (London, 1910).

Budge, E.A.W., *An Egyptian Hieroglyphic Dictionary*, 2 vols. (London, 1920).

Budge, E.A.W., *Facsimiles of Egyptian Hieratic Papyri in the British Museum, With Descriptions, Translations, etc.* (London, 1910).

Budge, E.A.W., *The Mummy* (New York, 1972), Collier Books ed.

Butzer, K.W., "Die Naturlandschaft Ägyptens während der Vorgeschichte und den dynastischen Zeitalter," *Akademie der Wissenschaften und der Literatur, Mainz, Math.-Naturwiss. Kl., Abhandlung* No. 2 (1959).

Caminos, R.A., *Late-Egyptian Miscellanies* (London, 1954).

Capart, J., and M. Werbrouck, *Memphis à l'ombre des pyramides* (Brussels, 1930).

Carter, H., *The Tomb of Tut-ankh-Amen*, Vol. 2 (London, 1927).

Cenival, J. L. de, "Un nouveau fragment de la Pierre de Palerme," *Bulletin de la Société Française d'Égyptologie*, Vol. 44 (1965), pp. 13-17.

Černý, J., *Ancient Egyptian Religion* (London, 1952, repr. 1957).

Chabas, F., *Le Papyrus Magique Harris* (Chalons-sur-Saône, 1860).

Chabas, F., *Mélanges égyptologiques*, 3rd Series, Vol. 2 (Chalons-sur-Saône and Paris, 1873), pp. 242-78.

Chace, A.B. *The Rhind Mathematical Papyrus*, 2 vols. (Oberlin, Ohio), 1927-29.

Champollion, J.F., *Lettres écrits d'Égypte et de Nubie en 1828 et 1829*, new ed. (Paris, 1868).

Champollion, J.F., *Monuments de l'Égypte et de la Nubie*, Vol. 1 (Paris, 1835).

Chassinat, E., *Le temple d'Edfou*, Vols. 2 and 3 (Cairo, 1918, 1928).

Clark, R.T.R., *Myth and Symbol in Ancient Egypt* (London, 1959; paperback ed., 1978).

Daressy, G., "La Pierre de Palerme et la chronologie de l'Ancien Empire," *BIFAO*, Vol. 12 (1916), pp. 161-214.

Daumas, F., see A. Barucq and.

David, R., *A Guide to Religious Ritual at Abydos* (Warminster, 1981).

Davies, N. de G., see Gardiner, A.H., and.

Davies, N. de G., *The Rock Tombs of El Amarna*, Part 6 (London, 1908).

# BIBLIOGRAPHY

Davies, N. de G., *The Temple of Hibis in El-Kargeh Oasis*, Part III, *The Decoration* (New York, 1952).

Derchain, P., *Le Papyrus Salt 825 (B.M. 10051), rituel pour la conservation de la vie en Égypte, Académie Royale de Belgique, Classe des Lettres, Mémoires*, Vol. 38 (Brussels, 1965).

Desroches-Nobelcourt, C., *Life and Death of a Pharaoh: Tutankhamen* (New York, 1963).

Drioton, E., "La religion égyptienne," in M. Brillant and R. Aigrain, eds., *Histoire des religions* (Paris, 1955), pp. 13-141.

Dümichen, J., *Altägyptische Tempelinschriften in den Jahren 1863-65*, Vol. 1 (Leipzig, 1867).

Edel, E., "Zur Lesung von 𓇳 'Regierungsjahr'," *JNES*, Vol. 8 (1949), pp. 35-39.

Edgerton, W.F., "Critical Note," *The American Journal of Semitic Languages and Literature*, Vol. 53 (1937), pp. 187-97.

Edwards, I.E.S., *British Museum, Hieroglyphic Texts from Egyptian Stelae*, Part VIII (London, 1939).

Emery, W.B., *Archaic Egypt* (Harmondsworth, England, 1961).

Emery, W.B., *Hor-aha* (Cairo, 1963)

Erman, A., "Ein Denkmal memphitischer Theologie," *Sitzungsberichte der Königlichen Akademie der Wissenschaften, Jahrgang 1911* (Berlin, 1911), pp. 916-50.

Erman, A., *The Ancient Egyptians: A Sourcebook of Their Writings*, tr. by A.M. Blackman; intro. by W.K. Simpson, Torchbook ed. (New York, 1966). Original title: *The Literature of the Ancient Egyptians* (London, 1927).

Erman, A., *A Handbook of Egyptian Religion* (London, 1907).

Erman, A., *Life in Ancient Egypt* (London, 1894)

Erman, A., *Die Märchen des Papyrus Westcar (Mittheilungen aus den orientalischen Sammlungen,* Hefte 5-6) (Berlin, 1890).

Erman, A., and H. Grapow, *Wörterbuch der ägyptischen Sprache,* 7 vols. (Leipzig, 1926-53); *Die Belegstellen,* 5 vols. (Leipzig, 1953). The whole work was reprinted in Berlin in 1971. It is abbreviated as *Wb.*

Faulkner, R.O., "The Bremner-Rhind Papyrus--III (and--IV)," *JEA,* Vol. 23 (1937), pp. 166-85; Vol. 24 (1938), pp. 41-53.

Faulkner, R.O., "The King and the Star-Religion in the Pyramid Texts," *JNES,* Vol. 25 (1966), pp. 153-61.

Faulkner, R.O., *The Ancient Egyptian Book of the Dead, Translated [into English],* Revised edition by C. Andrews (London, 1985). Published earlier by the Limited Editions Club under the title *The Book of the Dead. A Collection of Spells* (New York, 1972).

Faulkner, R.O., *The Ancient Egyptian Coffin Texts,* 3 vols. (Warminster, 1973-78).

Faulkner, R.O., *The Ancient Egyptian Pyramid Texts: Translated into English* (Oxford, 1969), with a *Supplement of Hieroglyphic Texts* (Oxford, 1969).

Faulkner, R.O., *A Concise Dictionary of Middle Egyptian* (Oxford, 1962).

Faulkner, R.O., *The Papyrus Bremner-Rhind (British Museum No. 10188): Bibliotheca Aegyptiaca* III (Brussels, 1933).

Fazzini, A., *Images for Eternity. Egyptian Art from Berkeley and Brooklyn* (New York, 1975).

Fischer, C.S., see Reisner, G.A., and.

Fischer, H.G., see Terrace, E.L.B., and.

Frankfort, H., *Ancient Egyptian Religion: An Interpretation* (New York, 1948).

Frankfort, H., *Kingship and the Gods* (Chicago, 1948).

Gardiner, A.H., "Horus the Beḥdetite," *JEA*, Vol. 30 (1944), pp. 23-60.

Gardiner, A.H., "The House of Life," *JEA*, Vol. 24 (1938), pp. 157-79.

Gardiner, A.H., "Hymns to Amon from a Leiden Papyrus," *ZÄS*, Vol. 42 (1905), pp. 12-42.

Gardiner, A.H., "Magic (Egyptian)," in J. Hastings, ed., *Encyclopedia of Religion and Ethics*, Vol. 8 (1915), pp. 262-69.

Gardiner, A.H., "The Mansion of Life and the Master of the King's Largesse," *JEA*, Vol. 24 (1938), pp. 83-91.

Gardiner, A.H., "Professional Magicians in Ancient Egypt," *PSBA*, Vol. 39 (1917), pp. 31-44, 138-40.

Gardiner, A.H., "Regnal Years and Civil Calendar in Pharaonic Egypt," *JEA*, Vol. 31 (1945), pp. 11-28.

Gardiner, A.H., "Some Personifications. I. *ḤỈKE*, The God of Magic," *PSBA*, Vol. 37 (1915), pp. 253-62.

Gardiner, A.H., "Some Personifications. II. *ḤU*, 'Authoritative Utterance.' *SIA*,' 'Understanding,' " *PSBA*, Vol. 38 (1916), pp. 43-54, 83-94.

Gardiner, A.H., *Ancient Egyptian Onomastica*, 3 vols. (Oxford, 1947).

Gardiner, A.H., *Egypt of the Pharaohs* (Oxford, 1961).

Gardiner, A.H., *Egyptian Grammar*, 3rd ed. (London, 1957).

Gardiner, A.H., *Egyptian Hieratic Texts: Series I. Literary Texts of the New Kingdom. Part I. The Papyrus Anastasi and the Papyrus Koller* (Leipzig, 1911).

Gardiner, A.H., *Hieratic Papyri in the British Museum. Third Series. Chester Beatty Gift*, 2 vols.

(London, 1935).

Gardiner, A.H., *Late-Egyptian Miscellanies* (Brussels, 1937).

Gardiner, A.H., *The Royal Canon of Turin* (Oxford, 1959).

Gardiner, A.H., and N. de G. Davies, *The Tomb of Amenemhet* (London, 1915).

Garstang, J., *Tombs of the Third Egyptian Dynasty* (Westminster, 1904).

Gauthier, H., "Quatre nouveaux fragments de la Pierre de Palerme," *Le Musée Égyptien*, Vol. 3 (1915), pp. 29-53.

Gauthier, H., *Le Livre des rois d'Égypte*, 5 vols. (Cairo, 1907-17).

Ghalioungui, P., see Habachi, L, and.

Ghalioungui, P., *The House of Life: Per Ankh. Magic and Medical Science in Ancient Egypt* (Amsterdam, 1963; 2nd ed., 1973).

Ghalioungui, P., *The Physicians of Pharaonic Egypt* (Cairo, 1983).

Giustolisi, V., "La 'Pietra di Palermo' e la cronologia dell' Antico Regno," *Sicilia archeologica*, Anno I, Nr. 4, Dec., 1968, pp. 5-14; Nr. 5, March, 1969, pp. 38-55; Anno II, Nr. 6, June, 1969, pp. 21-38.

Gödecken, K.B., *Eine Betrachtung der Inschriften des Meten im Rahmen der sozialen und rechtlichen Stellung von Privatleuten im ägyptischen Alten Reich* (Wiesbaden, 1976).

Godron, G., "Quel est le lieu de provenance de la 'Pierre de Palerme'?" *Chronique d'Égypte*, Vol. 27 (1952), pp. 17-22.

Goedicke, H., "Diplomatic Studies in the Old Kingdom," *Journal of the American Research Center in Egypt*, Vol. 3 (1964), pp. 31-41.

Goedicke, H., "Die Laufbahn des Mṯn," *MDAIK*, Vol. 21 (1966), pp. 1-71.

Golénisheff, W., ed., *Papyrus hiératiques (Catalogue général des antiquités du Musée du Caire: Nos. 58001-58036)*, Vol. 83 (Cairo, 1927).

Goyon, J.-C., see Parker, R.A.

Grapow, H., "Die Welt vor der Schöpfung," *ZÄS*, Vol. 67 (1931), pp. 34-38.

Grapow, H., *Grundriss der Medizin der alten Ägypter*, Vol. 1: *Anatomie und Physiologie* (Berlin, 1934).

Grapow, H., *Religiöse Urkunden (Urkunden des ägyptischen Altertums*, Abt. V [=*Urkunden* VI), 3 Heften (Leipzig, 1915-17).

Grapow, H., and W. Westendorf, "37. Wörterbücher, Repertorien, Schülerhandschriften," *Handbuch der Orientalistik*, Abt. 1, Vol. 1, Part 2 (Leiden, 1970), p. 221.

Grapow, H., see Erman A. and.

Grdseloff, B., "Notes sur deux monuments inédits de l'ancien empire," *ASAE*, Vol. 42 (1943), pp. 107-25.

Grébaut, E., *Hymne à Ammon-Ra* (Paris, 1874).

Griffith, F.Ll., "Notes on Egyptian Weights and Measures," *PSBA*, Vol. 14 (1891-92), pp. 403-50.

Griffith, F.Ll., and W.M.F. Petrie, *Two Hieroglyphic Papyri from Tanis* (London, 1889).

Griffith, F. Ll., and H. Thompson, *The Demotic Magical Papyrus of London and Leiden* (London, 1904).

Griffiths, J.G., see Plutarch.

Griffiths, J.G., *The Origins of Osiris and His Cult*, 2nd ed. (Leiden, 1980).

Habachi, L., "Khatâᶜna-Qantir: Importance," *ASAE*, Vol. 52 (1954), p. 450 et seq.

Habachi, L., and P. Ghalioungui, "Notes on Nine

Physicians of Pharaonic Egypt," *Bulletin de l'Institut d'Égypte*, Vol. 51 (1969), pp. 15-24.

Habachi, L., and P. Ghalioungui, "The 'House of Life' of Bubastis," *Chronique d'Égypte*, Vol. 46 (1971), pp. 59-71.

Hall, H.R., Review of A. de Buck's *De Egyptische Voorstellingen*, in *JEA*, Vol. 10 (1924), pp. 185-87.

Harris, J.R., *Lexicographical Studies in Ancient Egyptian Minerals* (Berlin, 1961).

Harris, J.R., see Lucas, A., and.

Hassan, S., *Hymnes religieux du moyen empire* (Cairo, 1928).

Hayes, W.C., *The Scepter of Egypt: A Background for the Study of the Egyptian Antiquities of the Metropolitan Museum of Art*, 2 vols. (New York, 1953-59).

Helck, W., "Bemerkungen zum Annalenstein," *MDAIK*, Vol. 30 (1974), pp. 31-35.

Helck, W., "Nilhöhe und Jubiläumsfest," *ZÄS*, Vol. 93 (1966), pp. 74-79.

Helck, W., *Die Lehre des Dwʾ-Ḥtjj* (Wiesbaden, 1970).

Helck, W., *Untersuchungen zu den Beamtentiteln des ägyptischen Alten Reiches* (Glückstadt / Hamburg / New York, 1954).

Helck, W., *Untersuchungen zu Manetho und den ägyptischen Königslisten* (Berlin, 1956).

Helck, W., see Sethe, K., *Urkunden der 18. Dynastie.*

Holmberg, M.S., *The God Ptah* (Lund and Copenhagen, 1946).

Hornung, E., "Chaotische Bereiche in der geordneten Welt," *ZÄS*, Vol. 81 (1956), pp. 28-32.

Hornung, E., *Der ägyptische Mythos von der*

*Himmelskuh: Ein Ätiologie des Unvollkommenen* (Göttingen, 1982).

Hornung, E., *Ägyptische Unterweltsbücher* (Munich, 1972, 2nd ed., 1984).

Hornung, E., *Das Amduat: Die Schrift des Verborgenen Raumes (Ägyptologische Abhandlungen*, Vols. 7, 13), 3 parts (Wiesbaden, 1963, 1967).

Hornung, E., *Das Buch der Anbetung des Re im Westen (Sonnenlitanei) (Aegyptiaca Helvetica*, Vol. 3), 2 parts (Geneva, 1975-76).

Hornung, E., *Conceptions of God in Ancient Egypt. The One and the Many* (Ithaca, 1982).

Hornung, E., with the assistance of A. Brodbeck and E. Staehelin, *Das Buch von den Pforten des Jenseits (Aegyptiaca Helvetica*, Vol. 7), 2 parts (Basel and Geneva, 1979-84).

Hornung, E. and C. Seeber, *Studien zum Sedfest* (Geneva, 1974).

Hurry, J.B., *Imhotep, the Vizier and Physician of King Zoser and Afterwards the Egyptian God of Medicine* (Oxford, 1926).

Iversen, E., *Papyrus Carlsberg Nr. VII: Fragments of a Hieroglyphic Dictionary* (Copenhagen, 1958).

James, T.G.H., *Pharaoh's People. Scenes from Life in Imperial Egypt* (Chicago and London, 1984).

Jenkins, N., *The Boat beneath the Pyramid: King Cheops' Royal Ship* (New York, 1980).

Jéquier, G., *Considérations sur les religions égyptiennes* (Neuchâtel, 1946).

Jéquier, G., *Le monument funéraire de Pepi II* (Cairo, 1936- ).

Jéquier, G., *La pyramide d'Oudjebten; Les pyramides des reines Neit et Apouit; La pyramide d'Aba* (Cairo, 1928-35).

Jonckheere, F., *Les médecins de l'Égypte pharaonique. Essai de prosopographie* (Brussels, 1958).

Junge, F., "Zur Fehldatierung des sog. Denkmals memphitischer Theologie oder Der Beitrag der ägyptischen Theologie zur Geistesgeschichte der Spätzeit," *MDAIK*, Vol. 29 (1973), pp. 195-204.

Junker, H., *Die Götterlehre von Memphis (Schabaka-Inschrift) (Aus den Abhandlungen der Preussischen Akademie der Wissenschaften, Jahrgang 1939, Phil.-hist. Klasse*, Nr. 23) (Berlin, 1940).

Kaiser, W., "Einige Bemerkungen zur ägyptischen Frühzeit. II. Zur Frage einer über Menes hinausreichenden ägyptischen Geschichtsüberlieferung," *ZÄS*, Vol. 86 (1961), pp. 39-61.

Kaplony, P., "Gottespalast und Götterfestungen in der ägyptischen Frühzeit," *ZÄS*, Vol. 88 (1962), pp. 5-16.

Kaplony, P., *Die Inschriften der ägyptischen Frühzeit*, Vols. 1-3 (Wiesbaden, 1963); *Supplementband* (Wiesbaden, 1964).

Kaplony, P., *Kleine Beiträge zu den Inschriften der ägyptischen Frühzeit* (Wiesbaden, 1966).

Kees, H., "Archaisches [tt-ᵗtt] 'Erzieher'?," *ZÄS*, Vol. 82 (1957), pp. 58-62.

Kees, H., "Die Feuerinsel in Sargtexten und im Totenbuch," *ZÄS*, Vol. 78 (1942), pp. 41-63.

Kees, H., "Toten-Literatur. 20. Pyramidentexte," *Handbuch der Orientalistik*, Abt. 1, Vol. 1, Part 2 (Leiden, 1970), pp. 52-60; "21. Sargtexte und Totenbuch," *Ibid.*, pp. 61-69.

Kees, H., *Ancient Egypt* (Chicago and London, 1961; Phoenix ed., 1977).

Kees, H., *Der Götterglaube im alten Ägypten*, 2nd ed. (Berlin, 1956).

Kees, H., *Totenglauben und Jenseitsvorstellungen*

*der alten Ägypter* (Leipzig, 1956; 4th print., 1980).

Kees, H., see Bissing, F.W. von.

Kitchen, K.A., *Pharaoh Triumphant, The Life and Times of Ramesses II* (Warminster, England, 1982).

Kitchen, K.A., *The Third Intermediate Period in Egypt (1100-650 B.C.)* (Warminster, 1973)

Köhler, U., *Das Imiut*, 2 vols. (Wiesbaden, 1975).

Lacau, P., "Textes religieux égyptiens," *Receuil de travaux relatifs à la philologie et à l'archéologie égyptiennes et assyriennes*, Vols. 26-37 (1904-15), partially reprinted in *Textes religieux égyptiens* (Paris, 1910).

Lacau, P., and J. P. Lauer, *Fouilles à Saqqara; la pyramide à degrés*, Vol. 4: *Inscriptions gravées sur les vases* (Cairo, 1959-61).

Lange, H.O, *Der magische Papyrus Harris* (Copenhagen, 1927).

Lanzone, R.V., *Dizionario di mitologia egizia*, 3 vols. (Turin, 1881-86; reprint, Amsterdam, 1974, with a fourth previously unpublished volume, 1975).

Lauer, J.P., *Saqqara: The Royal Cemetery of Memphis. Excavations and Discoveries since 1850* (London, 1976).

Leclant, J., "Recherches récentes sur les Textes des Pyramides et les pyramides à textes de Saqqarah," *Académie Royale de Belgiques: Bulletin de la Classe des Lettres et des Sciences Morales et Politiques*, 5e série, Tome LXXI (1985, 10-11), pp. 292-305

Leclant, J., see Parker, R.A.

Lefebvre, G., "L'oeuf divin d'Hermopolis," *ASAE*, Vol. 23 (1923), pp. 65-67.

Lefebvre, G., *Tableau des parties du corps humain mentionnées par les égyptiens (Supplément aux Annales du Service des Antiquités, 17)* (Cairo, 1952).

Lefebvre, G., *Le tombeau de Petosiris* (Cairo, 1923-24).

Lepsius, C.R., *Denkmäler aus Ägypten und Äthiopien*, Abt. I-VI (Berlin 1849-58; photographic reprint, Geneva, 1972); Text, 5 vols., ed. E. Naville et al. (Leipzig, 1897-1913; phot. repr., Geneva, 1975).

Lepsius, C.R., *Das Todtenbuch der Ägypter nach dem hieroglyphischen Papyrus in Turin* (Turin and Leipzig, 1842; repr. Osnabrück, 1969).

Lepsius, C.R., *Über die Götter der vier Elemente bei den Ägyptern* (Berlin, 1856).

Lesko, L.H., *The Ancient Egyptian Book of Two Ways* (Berkeley/Los Angeles/London, 1972).

Lexa, F., *La magie dans l'Égypte antique de l'Ancien Empire jusqu'à l'Époque Copte*, Vol. 2 (Paris, 1925).

Lichtheim, M., *Ancient Egyptian Literature*, 3 vols. (Berkeley/Los Angeles/London, 1975-80).

Lucas, A., and J.R. Harris, *Ancient Egyptian Materials and Industries* (London, 1962).

Lythgoe, A.M., "Excavations at the South Pyramid at Lisht in 1914," *Ancient Egypt*, 1915, pp. 145-53.

Málek, J., see Baines, J. and.

Manetho, see Wadell, W.G.

Mariette, A., *Dendérah*, 5 vols. (Paris, 1870-80).

Mariette, A., *Les mastabas de l'Ancien Empire*, ed. by G. Maspero (Paris, 1882-89).

Mariette, A., *Les papyrus égyptiens du Musée de Boulaq*, Vol. 2 (Paris, 1872).

Maspero, G., "La carrière administrative de deux hauts fonctionnaires égyptiens," *Études égyptiennes*, Vol. 2 (1890), pp. 113-272.

Maspero, G., "De quelques termes d'architecture

égyptienne," *PSBA*, Vol. 11 (1889), pp. 304-17.

Maystre, C., *Le livre de la vache du ciel dans les tombeaux de la Valle des Rois, BIFAO*, Vol. 40 (Cairo, 1940).

Maystre, C., and A. Piankoff, *Le livre des portes*, 3 vols. (Cairo, 1939-62).

Mercer, S.A.B., *Horus, Royal God of Egypt* (London, 1942).

Meyer, E., "Gottesstaat, Militärherrschaft und Ständewesen in Ägypten," *Sitzungsberichte der Preussischen Akademie der Wissenschaften. Jahrgang 1928. Phil.-hist. Klasse* (Berlin 1928), pp. 495-532.

Meyer, E., *Ägyptische Chronologie* (Berlin, 1904).

Montet, P., *Everyday Life in the Days of Ramesses the Great* (Philadelphia, 1981).

Morenz, S., *Egyptian Religion* (Ithaca, 1973).

Moret, A., "La Légende d'Osiris à l'époque thébaine d'après l'hymne à Osiris du Louvre," *BIFAO*, Vol. 30 (1931), pp. 725-50, and plates I-III.

Moret, A., *Du charactère religieux de la royauté pharaonique (Annales du Musée Guimet: Bibliothèque d'études*, Vol. 15) (Paris, 1902).

Moret, A., *Le rituel du cult divin journalier en Égypte* (Paris, 1902).

Moss, R.L.B., see Porter, B., and.

Müller, H., *Die formale Entwicklung der Titulatur der ägyptischen Könige* (Glückstadt/Hamburg/New York, 1938).

Murnane, W.J., *United with Eternity. A Concise Guide to the Monuments of Medinet Habu* (Chicago and Cairo, 1980).

Murray, M.A., *Index of Names and Titles of the Old Kingdom* (London, 1908).

Naville, E., "The Litany of Ra," in S. Birch, ed.,

*Records of the Past: Being English Translations of the Assyrian and Egyptian Monuments*, Vol. 8 (London, 1876), pp. 103-28.

Naville, E., "La Pierre de Palerme," *Recueil de travaux relatifs à la philologie et à l'archéologie égyptiennes et assyriennes*, 25me année (1903), pp. 64-81.

Naville, E., *Das ägyptische Todtenbuch der XVII. bis XX. Dynastie aus verschiedenen Urkunden zusammengestellt und herausgegeben*, 3 vols. (Berlin, 1886).

Naville, E., *La Litanie du Soleil: Inscriptions recueillies dans les tombeaux des rois à Thèbes* (Leipzig, 1875).

Neugebauer, O., and R.A. Parker, *Egyptian Astronomical Texts*, 3 vols. (Providence, Rhode Island, and London, 1960-69).

Newberry, P.E., "The Set Rebellion of the IInd Dynasty," *Ancient Egypt*, 1922, pp. 40-46.

Newberry, P.E., and G.A. Wainwright, "King Udy-mu (Den) and the Palermo Stone," *Ancient Egypt*, 1914, pp. 148-55.

Nims, C.F., *Thebes of the Pharaohs, Pattern for Every City* (London, 1965).

O'Mara, P.F., *The Chronology of the Palermo and Turin Canons* (La Canada, Calif., 1980).

O'Mara, P.F., *The Palermo Stone and the Archaic Kings of Egypt* (La Canada, Calif., 1979).

Otto, E., *Das ägyptische Mundöffnungsritual*, 2 vols. (Wiesbaden, 1960).

Otto, E., *Egyptian Art and the Cults of Osiris and Amon* (London, 1968).

Parker, R.A.. "Egyptian Chronology," in "Egypt," *Encyclopedia Americana*, Vol. 10, pp. 32-33.

Parker, R.A., J. Leclant, and J.-C. Goyon, *The Edifice of Taharqa by the Sacred Lake of Karnak (Brown Egyptological Studies*, VII) (Providence, Rhode Island, and London, 1979).

Parker, R.A., see Neugebauer, O., and.

Patrick, R., *All Color Book of Egyptian Mythology* (London, 1972).

Peet, T.E., Review of Borchardt's *Die Annalen* in *JEA*, Vol. 6 (1920), pp. 149-54.

Pellegrini, A., "Nota sopra un'iscrizione egizia del Museo di Palermo," *Archivio storico siciliano*, n. s., Anno xx (1895), pp. 297-316.

Petrie, W.M.F., "The Earliest Inscriptions," *Ancient Egypt*, 1914, pp. 61-77.

Petrie, W.M.F., "New Portions of the Annals," *Ancient Egypt*, 1916, pp. 114-20.

Petrie, W.M.F., *History of Egypt*, Vol. 1 (XIth ed. rev., London, 1924).

Petrie, W.M.F., *The Making of Egypt* (London and New York, 1939).

Petrie, W.M.F., *The Royal Tombs of the Earliest Dynasties*, Part II (London, 1901).

Petrie, W.M.F., *The Royal Tombs of the First Dynasty*, Part I (London, 1900).

Petrie, W.M.F., see Griffith, F.Ll., and.

Piankoff, A., *The Litany of Re (Bollingen Series*, Vol. 40.4) (New York, 1964).

Piankoff, A., *Le livre des quererts* (Cairo, 1946); published earlier in *BIFAO*, Vols. 41-45 (1942-47).

Piankoff, A., *Mythological Papyri, Edited with a Chapter on the Symbolism of the Papyri by N. Rambova (Bollingen Series*, Vol. 40.3) (New York, 1957).

Piankoff, A., *The Pyramid of Unas (Bollingen Series*, Vol. 40.5) (Princeton, 1968).

Piankoff, A., *The Shrines of Tut-Ankh-Amon* (*Bollingen Series*, Vol. 40.2) (Princeton, 1955).

Piankoff, A., *The Tomb of Ramesses VI*, ed. by N. Rambova (*Bollingen Series*, Vol. 40.1) (New York, 1954).

Piankoff, A., see Maystre, C., and.

Pirenne, J., *Histoire de la civilisation de l'Égypte ancienne* (Neuchâtel, 1961).

Plutarch, *De Iside et Osiride*, ed., transl., and comm. by J. G. Griffiths (Cardiff, 1970).

Porter, B., and R.L.B. Moss, *Topographical Bibliography of Ancient Egyptian Hieroglyphic Texts, Reliefs, and Paintings*, Vols. 1-3, 2nd ed. (Oxford, 1960-78).

Posener, G., *De la divinité du pharaon* (Paris, 1960).

Posener, G., *Ostraca hiératiques littéraires de Deir el Medineh*, Vol. 2 (Cairo, 1951).

Posener, G., et al., *Dictionnaire de la civilisation égyptienne*, 2nd ed. (Paris, 1970).

Pritchard, J.B., ed., *Ancient Near Eastern Texts Relating to the Old Testament* (Princeton, 1950), with the translations of many Egyptian texts by J.A. Wilson.

Quibell, J.E., *Hierakonpolis*, Part 1, with Notes by W.M.F. Petrie (London, 1900).

Quibell, J.E., and F.W. Green, *Hierakonpolis*, Part 2 (London, 1902).

Ranke, H., *Die ägyptischen Personennamen*, Vol. 2 (Glückstadt/Hamburg/New York, 1952).

Read, F.W., "Nouvelles remarques sur la Pierre de Palerme," *BIFAO*, Vol. 12 (1916), pp. 215-22.

Redford, D.B., *Pharaonic King-lists, Annals and Day-Books: A Contribution to the Study of the Egyptian Sense of History* (Mississauga, Ontario, Canada, 1986).

BIBLIOGRAPHY

Reeves, C.N., "A Fragment of Fifth Dynasty Annals at University College London," *Göttinger Miszellen. Beiträge zur ägyptologischen Diskussion*, Heft 32 (1979), pp. 47-50.

Reisner, G.A., "A Scribe's Tablet Found by the Hearst Expedition at Giza," *ZÄS*, Vol. 48 (1911), pp. 113-14.

Reisner, G.A., *A History of Giza Necropolis*, Vol. 1 (Cambridge, Mass., and London, 1942).

Reisner, G.A., and C.S. Fischer, "Preliminary Report on the Work of the Harvard-Boston Expedition in 1911-13," *ASAE*, Vol. 13 (1914), pp. 227-52.

Roeder, G., "Die Kosmogonie von Hermopolis," *Egyptian Religion*, Vol. 1 (1933), pp. 1-37.

Roeder, G., "Zwei hieroglyphische Inschriften aus Hermopolis (Ober-Ägypten)," *ASAE*, Vol. 52 (1954), pp. 315-74.

Roeder, G., *Urkunden zur Religion des alten Ägypten* (Jena, 1923).

Sandman, M., *Texts from the Time of Akhenaten (Bibliotheca Aegyptiaca* VIII) (Brussels, 1938).

Sandman Holmberg, M., see Holmberg, M.S.

Sauneron, S., *Esna*, Vol. 3: *Le temple d'Esna* (Cairo, 1968); Vol. 5: *Les fêtes religieuses d'Esna aux derniers siècles du Paganisme* (Cairo, 1962).

Sauneron, S., *Le Papyrus magique illustré de Brooklyn* (New York, 1970).

Sauneron, S., *Les prêtres de l'ancienne Égypte* (Paris, 1957).

Sauneron, S., and J. Yoyotte, "La naissance du monde selon l'Égypte ancienne," *Sources orientales*: Vol. 1, *La naissance du monde* (Paris, 1959), pp. 19-91.

Schack-Schackenburg, H., *Das Buch von den Zwei Wegen des seligen Toten* (Leipzig, 1903).

Schäfer, H., "Ein Bruchstück altägyptischer Annalen," *Abhandlungen der Königlichen Preussischen Akademie der Wissenschaften, 1902. Phil.-hist. Abh.* (Berlin, 1902), pp. 3-41.

Schäfer, H., *Ägyptische Inschriften aus den Königlichen Museen zu Berlin*, Vol. 1 (Leipzig, 1913).

Schäfer, H., and W. Andrae, *Die Kunst des alten Orients* (Berlin, 1935).

Schlögel, H.A., *Der Gott Tatenen* (Freiburg, Switz., and Göttingen, 1980).

Schweitzer, U., *Das Wesen des Ka im Diesseits und Jenseits der alten Ägypter (Ägyptologische Forschungen*, Heft 19) (Glückstadt/Hamburg/New York, 1956).

Seeber, C., see Hornung, E., and.

Seele, K.C., see Steindorff, G., and.

Sethe, K., "Hitherto Unnoticed Evidence Regarding Copper Works of Art of the Oldest Period of Egyptian History," *JEA*, Vol. 1 (1914), pp. 233-36.

Sethe, K., *Ägyptische Lesestücke* (Leipzig, 1924, 2nd ed., 1928).

Sethe, K., *Die altägyptischen Pyramidentexte*, 4 vols. (Leipzig, 1908-22).

Sethe, K., *Amun und die acht Urgötter von Hermopolis: Eine Untersuchung über Ursprung und Wesen des ägyptischen Götterkönigs* (Berlin, 1929).

Sethe, K., *Dramatische Texte zu altägyptischen Mysterienspielen (Untersuchungen zur Geschichte und Altertumskunde Ägyptens*, Vol. 10) (Leipzig, 1928; repr. Hildesheim, 1964).

Sethe, K., *Erläuterungen zu den ägyptischen Lesestücken* (Leipzig, 1927).

Sethe, K., *Übersetzung und Kommentar zu den altägyptischen Pyramidentexten*, 6 vols. (Hamburg,

1962).

Sethe, K., *Untersuchungen zur Geschichte und Altertumskunde Ägyptens*, Vol. 3: *Beiträge zur ältesten Geschichte Ägyptens* (Leipzig, 1905).

Sethe, K., *Urkunden der 18. Dynastie (Urkunden des ägyptischen Altertums, IV,* [=*Urkunden* IV]), 4 vols. (Leipzig, 1906-09, 2nd ed., 1927-30); continued by W. Helck, Vols. 5-6 (Berlin, 1955-58); paginated continuously.

Sethe, K., *Urkunden des Alten Reichs*, Vol. 1, 2nd ed. (Leipzig, 1933) (=*Urkunden* I).

Simpson, W.K., *The Literature of Ancient Egypt* (New Haven and London, 1971, new ed. 1973).

Simpson, W.K., see W.S. Smith, *The Art and Architecture of Ancient Egypt.*

Smith, W.S., *The Art and Architecture of Ancient Egypt*, revised with additions by W.K. Simpson (Harmondsworth, 1981).

Smith, W.S., *A History of Egyptian Sculpture and Painting in the Old Kingdom*, 2nd ed. (Boston, 1940).

Spencer, A.J., *Death in Ancient Egypt* (Harmondsworth, 1982).

Spencer, P., *The Egyptian Temple: A Lexicographical Study* (London / Boston / Melbourne / Henley, 1984).

Steindorff, G., and K.C. Seele, *When Egypt Ruled the East* (revised ed., Chicago and London, 1957).

Stewart, H.M., "Traditional Egyptian Sun Hymns of the New Kingdom," *Bulletin of the Institute of Archaeology*, University of London, Vol. 6 (1967), pp. 29-74.

Stewart, H.M., *Egyptian Stelae, Reliefs and Paintings from the Petrie Collection. Part Two: Archaic Period to Second Intermediate Period* (Warminster,

1979).

Te Velde, H., *Seth, God of Confusion* (Leiden, 1977).

Terrace, E.L.B., and H.G. Fischer, *Treasures of Egyptian Art from the Cairo Museum* (New York and Los Angeles, 1970).

Thompson, H., see Griffith, F.Ll., and.

Uphill, E.P., *The Temple of Per Ramesses* (Warminster, 1984).

Vandier, J., *Manuel d'archéologie égyptienne*, Vol. 1 (Paris, 1952).

Vandier, J., *La religion égyptienne* (Paris, 1949).

Vareille, A., "L'hymne au soleil des architectes d'Amenophis III Souti et Hor," *BIFAO*, Vol. 41 (1942), pp. 25-30, and plates I-II.

Vernus, P., "Name," *Lexikon der Ägyptologie*, Vol. 4, cc. 320-26.

Volten, A., *Demotische Traumdeutung (Pap. Carlsberg XIII und XIV verso), Analecta aegyptiaca*, Vol. 3 (Copenhagen, 1942).

von Känel, F., *Les prêtres-ouâb de Sekhmet et les conjurateurs de Serket* (Paris, 1984).

Wadell, W.G., *Manetho with an English Translation* (London and Cambridge, Mass., 1940, repr. 1980).

Wainwright, G.A., "The Origin of Amun," *JEA*, Vol. 49 (1963), pp. 21-23.

Wainwright, G.A., Review of K. Sethe's *Amun und die acht Urgötter von Hermopolis* in *JEA*, Vol. 17 (1931), pp. 151-52.

Wainwright, G.A., see Newberry, P.E., and.

Ward, W.A., *Index of Egyptian Administrative and Religious Titles of the Middle Kingdom* (Beirut, 1982).

# BIBLIOGRAPHY

Weber, M., *Beiträge zur Kenntnis des Schrift- und Buchwesens der alten Ägypter* (Cologne, 1969).

Weigall, A., *A History of the Pharaohs*, Vol. 1 (New York, 1925).

Weill, R., *Le champ des roseaux et le champ des offrandes dans la religion funéraire et la religion générale* (Paris, 1936).

Werbrouck, M., see Capart, J., and.

Westendorf, W., see Grapow, H., and.

Wilkinson, C.K., and M. Hill, *Egyptian Wall Paintings: The Metropolitan Museum of Art's Collection of Facsimiles* (New York, 1983).

Wilson, J.A., "Egypt," in H. and H.A. Frankfort, J.A. Wilson, T. Jacobsen, and W.A. Irwin, *The Intellectual Adventure of Ancient Man* (Chicago and London, 1946; Phoenix ed., 1977).

Wilson, J.A., see Pritchard, J.B.

Wolf, W., "Der Berliner Ptah-Hymnus (P 3048, II-XII.)," *ZÄS*, Vol. 64 (1929), pp. 17-44.

Yoyotte, J., see Sauneron, S., and.

Žabkar, L.V., *A Study of the Ba Concept in Ancient Egyptian Texts* (Chicago, 1968).

Zandee, J., "The Book of Gates," *Studies in the History of Religions (Supplements to Numen)*, XVII: *Liber amicorum, Studies in Honour of Professor Dr. C. J. Bleeker* (Leiden, 1969), pp. 282-324.

Zandee, J., "Das Schöpferwort im alten Ägypten," *Verbum: Essays on Some Aspects of the Religious Function of Words dedicated to Dr. H.W. Obbink* (Rheno-Traiectina, Vol. 6, 1964), pp. 33-66.

Zandee, J., *Hymnen aan Amon van Papyrus Leiden I 350* (Leiden, 1948).

# Index of Egyptian Words

In the following index the two kinds of "s" are ordinarily grouped together, the distinction between them being given only when I have made that distinction for "ś" in the text, which is usually in connection with Old-Kingdom words. Note also that when "z" has been used by the authors I have quoted, then I have given that transcription under "z". In line with this I have also paid attention to the varying transcription techniques used by other authors whom I have quoted (e.g., see the different forms under *Ij-mr.s* and note that "*j*" is often written for either "*i*" or "*y*"). Further, I have given the few instances when phonetic transcriptions of proper names appear. However, the reader should consult the index of proper names for a much more complete list of such names. When I or other authors have added vowels to Egyptian words, they appear in the other index.

*ꜥꜥw:* 519
*ỉwdt:* 247
*ỉḫt:* 217
*ỉḥ, ỉḫt, ỉḥw:* 97, 248, 327, 443, 481, 518, 579
*ỉḥỉḥw:* 544
*ỉṯt:* 6

ꜣ, ꜣꜣ

*iꜣw:* 252
*Ꜣ-t:* 84
*Ꜣ't-Sbk:* 152, 159-60, 162
*Ꜣj-mr.s* or *Yy-mrs:* 152, 159-60, 162
*iwf* or *if:* 255
*iw.f-n-nri* or *iw.f-m-nri:* 248
*Ꜣwnw-Rᶜ:* 253
*ipwr:* 255
*imy-wnwt:* 24
*imy-wt:* 8, 54, 72, 115-16
*imj.t-pr:* 168
*imy-ẖt:* 255
*imy Snwt:* 36
*imy-r ḥkꜣw:* 24
*imyt-r swnw:* 40
*imyt-r swnwt:* 40
*imn:* 508, 564
*inb:* 254
*Ꜣnpw-ḥtp:* 173
*Ꜣnpw-m-ᶜnẖ:* 163-65
*Ꜣntyw:* 72, 120-21
*iry-iẖt:* 152, 163
*iry-pᶜt:* 248
*irw:* 250, 364, 481, 496, 517
*irw ṯkt:* 250
*irt wpt-r:* 101
*ir.t bin.t:* 337
*irp n Ḳmt:* 255
*iẖty (ᶜẖwty):* 251
*iẖiẖw:* 540, 544
*is:* 35

*Mtn:* Doc. I.2, pass.
*md⟨t:* 472
*mdⁱt:* 25, 27, 35, 251
*mdḫw:* 250

~~~~

*n-nbw:* 118
*Nj-mⁱᶜt-Ḥp* (or *Ḥᶜpj*) or *N-mⁱᶜ.t-ḫⁱp:* 159-61
*Nj-swtḫ:* 170
*nisw:* 24, 146
*nᶜr:* 4
*nw* (abyss): 298, 420, 431, 437-38, 445, 459, 461, 467,
        566, 588
*nw, nwy(t):* 247-48, 261
*nw*-god: 518
*nwb:* 129
*nb:* 7
*Nb.š* or *Nbsnt* or *Nb-snt:* 168, 170-71
*nbi:* 316
*nbdy:* 250
*npt(?):* 254
*Nfrii:* 227-28
*nfr(t):* 252
*nmst:* 420
*Nn-nsw:* 253
*nhy:* 347, 608
*nht:* 347, 608
*Nḥb-kⁱw:* 291
*nḥḥ:* 304, 314, 370, 457, 459, 467, 509, 542, 546,
        553, 557, 563, 566, 575-79, 624,
*nḫb* (a kind of land): 248, 562
*nḫn:* 252
*Nḫn,* also later *Mḫn:* 253

◻

⧝

*ḫd:* 136
*ḫḏ:* 348, 608

●

*ẖꜣ* (office): 35
*ẖꜣ* (land measure): 56, 159, 162-63
*ẖꜣy:* 24
*ẖꜣy n(?) rmnyw:* 251
*ẖpr, ẖprt, ẖprw:* 314, 374, 376, 455, 478, 480, 496,
        500-02, 505, 517, 520-21, 571, 587
*ẖm-n:* 327, 580
*ẖmnw:* 298, 327, 580
*ẖmt:* 255
*ẖntt:* 25
*ẖrp Srḳt:* 24
*Ḥsf-nṯrw:* 114
*ẖt* (probably for *ẖtiw*): 254
*ẖt-ꜥꜣ:* 218

⊷

*ẖꜣ:* 161
*ẖꜥḳw:* 250
*ẖnini:* 247
*ẖnm(t):* 247
*ẖr-ꜥw:* 180
*ẖr-ẖb:* 23
*ẖr md:* 168
*ẖry.ẖbt:* 23, 205, 209
*ẖry-ẖpš:* 255
*ẖkrw:* 481

—, ⌐

*sr:* 160
*srw:* 230
*srft:* 254
*srmt:* 247
*Srḫt:* 24
*sḥm(t):* 248
*sḫm:* 416, 516
*sḫm-nṯrw:* 114
*Šḫmw:* 153, 170
*sḫpr:* 374, 376, 481, 522
*sḫn:* 255
*sḫrw n ib-f:* 306
*Šḫtj:* 114
*sḫnn:* 254
*sš :* 24-25, 27, 40, and see *zš* below
*sš pr mdꜣt nṯr:* 25
*sš nt ḥsb:* 24
*sš ḥsb:* 24
*sš šꜥt n Ḥr kꜣ nḫt:* 248
*sš ḳdy:* 251
*sš tꜣy mdꜣt:* 27
*sšꜣ:* 250
*Sšꜣt:* 25, 125
*sšm-tꜣ :* 168
*sšm-tꜣ ḥḳꜣ.t:* 157
*skꜣ(t):* 254
*sk(i):* 251
*stꜣt, stꜣwt:* 56, 88, 137-39, 163
*sty itn:* 247
*stwt (?) n sḫt:* 255
*sd:* 136, 607

⊐

◻

# Index of Proper Names and Subjects

I have not indexed the Chronology or the Bibliography since each of those lists is an independent unit so organized as to be easily consulted. I have not indexed in a detailed way subjects in the documents attached to the second chapter (or their introductions) since the subject matter of those documents was described rather thoroughly in the second chapter and hence the reader can readily see references to the proper places in the documents when reading Chapter Two. Nor have I have included all the rather fictional names of caverns and cities in the Netherworld and names or titles of the gods based on their attributes or powers. However, the indexing of the more common proper names in those documents is quite complete. Note that the Index of Egyptian Words can serve as a supplement to the subject indexing presented here in this index. In general, I have not indexed the names of cities or countries when they are incidental to the account. I have not indexed (except in rare instances) the long list of names and things in Doc. I.9, though the Egyptian equivalents when given are indexed in the Index of Egyptian Words. But I have indexed the categories of items found in that document. In this index I ordinarily give only the name of authors cited and not the titles of their works. However, in some cases where there are a great many citations (as with Gardiner, Helck, or Sethe), I have separated the entries by using abbreviated titles, The full titles may be readily identified by consulting the pages cited or the Bibliography.

391, 418, 466, and see Horus falcon; Horian dreams, 604, 613; the Followers of, 12, 97, 357; the Following of, 11, 48, 50-51, 65, 68-71, 75-82, 103-04; Horus as creator god at Edfu, 264, as primitive creator god, 279-84; on his throne, 499; the myth of the genealogy of, 282-84, 289-90, 292, 380, 383, 408, 420, 477; the secret forms of, 478, 500-01; and see mounds of, and Eye of

    Horus at the Head of the Spirits, 423

    Horus Bull, 55, 85

    Horus falcon, 279, 281, 283, 331, 413; king's title or representation, 3, 5, 7-8, 118-19, 138, 379, 400

    Horus in *Snwt* (or Shenwet), 28, 36, 337

    Horus Mekhantenirti, 293, 588, 593

    Horus-name of the king, 7, 118-19, and Doc. I.1 passim

    Horus of Buto, 138

    Horus of Dunanu, a falcon god, 139

    Horus of the Heron of Djebakherut (or Buto), 89

    Horus-of-Gold name of the king, 93, 118, 129

    Horus of Hasroet, 102

    Horus of Heaven, 55, 77, 130, 281, 283

    Horus of Letopolis, 385

    Horus of Pe, 138

    Horus of Sezmet, 415, 427

    Horus of the East, 415, 427

    Horus of the Gods, 415, 427

    Horus of the Horizon, 281, 427

    Horus of the Netherworld, 421, 499

    Horus the Behdetite, 379

    Horus the Elder, 141, 294 (alluded to), 383-84

    Horus the Praiser, 473, 492, 495

    Horus-Seth, 88, 90-91, 119, 131, 138

    hour goddesses, 482

    hour watchers (astronomers), 24, 250

creator gods, 281, 370, 415

lotus, 359; lotus-barks, 360, 441, 473; the primitive Hermopolitan flower, 297, 302, 413, 420, 425, 454, 467; emergence of Re from, 302, 460

Louvre Museum, 7, 29

Lucas, A., 116-17

Luxor, 46, 319, 375, 394, 400

Lythgoe, A.M., 115


*Maat*, right, truth, or order, xi-xii, 23, 32, 265, 282, 300, 306, 315-16, 328, 351, 413, 441, 446, 448, 455, 459, 554, 556-60; as the daughter of Atum or Re or as a personified goddess of justice or order, 282, 288-89, 384, 390, 396-97, 401, 438, 446, 483, 488, 624

Madjoi, 556-57

Mafdet, 55, 74, 128

magic and magicians, 13, 19, 22-24, 28-30, 33-34, 185, 203, 205-07, 210-11, 214, 216, 226, 239, 263, 294, 321-22, 327, 334-42, 349-50, 361, 389-90, 400-01, 409, 413-14, 417, 421, 433, 438, 455, 469, 476, 532, 541-42, 546; effectiveness of magical spells, 23, 336-37, 438, 464, 493, 507, 541, 591; Isis and, 331, 336, 366, 476, 499, 509; the magical power of gods, 335-41, 346, 348-50, 399, 430, 463, 476, 481, 499, 507-09, 524, 532-33, 540-41, 616-21, 623; Thoth and, 300, 304, 335-37, 350; and Docs. I.6, ,II.11 passim, and see Heka, and Hike

Magnate of the Ten of Upper Egypt, 15, 38, 151, 157

Malachite country, 54, 92

Málek, see Baines, J.

man, his nature, 354-55; his vivification, 334; and see creation (of man)

Manetho, 97, 99, 106

Mansion of Atum, 495

# Illustrations

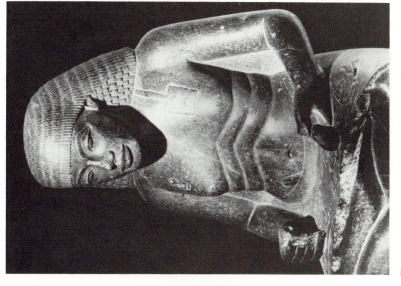

Fig. I.1c   Statue of Amenhotep, son of Hapu, as a scribe. Dynasty 18. Cairo Museum. After Terrace and Fischer, *Treasures of Egyptian Art from the Cairo Museum*, p. 119.

Fig. I.1b   Another seated scribe. Dynasty 5. Louvre Museum. Photograph by Sue Clagett.

Fig. I.1a   A seated scribe. Dynasty 6. Pelizaeus Museum, Hildesheim.

Fig. I.2b   A scribe in the act of recording an inventory. Dynasty 5. Cropped from the photograph in Pirenne, *Histoire de la civilization de l'Égypte ancienne*, Vol. 1, pl. after p. 140, with the permission of Les Éditions de Baconnière, Boudry, Suisse.

Fig. I.2a   Wooden panels from niches in the west wall of the tomb of Hesyre in Saqqara. Dynasty 3. Cairo Museum.

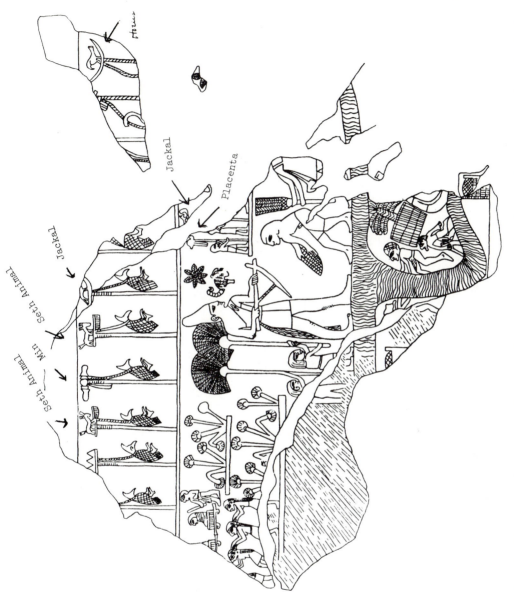

Horus

Jackal

Placenta

Jackal

Seth Animal

Min

Seth Animal

Seth Animal

Fig. I.3a  Mace-head of King Scorpion. Predynastic. Drawn from the Original in the Ashmolean Museum, Oxford, after Smith, *A History of Egyptian Sculpture and Painting in the Old Kingdom*, Fig. 30. Copied with the permission of the Museum of Fine Arts in Boston.

Fig. I.3b   The Mace-head of King Scorpion reconstructed.

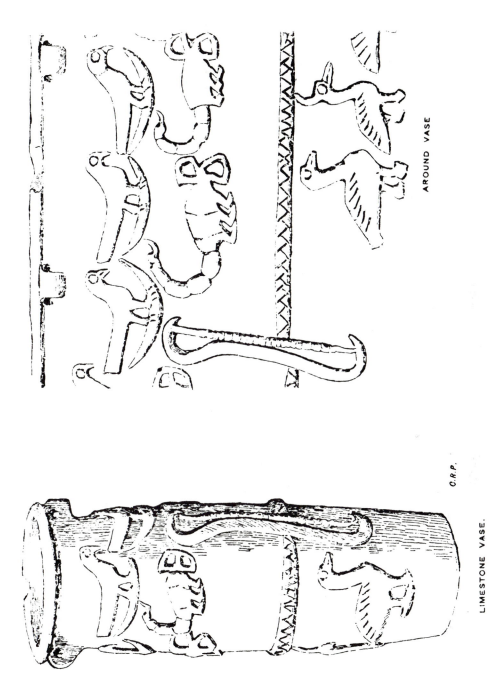

AROUND VASE

LIMESTONE VASE.

C.R.P.

Fig. I.4a   Vase with the name of the Horus Scorpion. Predynastic. Cf. J. E. Quibell, *Hierakonpolis*, Vol. 1, pl. XIX.

Fig. I.4b   Group of early maces and vase. Restored after Quibell, *ibid.*, Vol. 1, pl. XXV.

# THE ALPHABET

| SIGN | TRANS-LITERATION | OBJECT DEPICTED | APPROXIMATE SOUND-VALUE | REMARKS |
|---|---|---|---|---|
| | ꜣ | Egyptian vulture | (the glottal stop heard at the commencement of German words beginning with a vowel, ex. *der Adler.* | corresponds to Hebrew א *ʾāleph* and to Arabic أ *ʾalif hamzatum.* |
| | ỉ | flowering reed | usually consonantal *y*; at the beginning of words sometimes identical with *ꜣ*. | corresponds to Hebrew י *yōdh*, Arabic ي *yā.* |
| (1) (2) | y | (1) two reed-flowers (2) oblique strokes | *y* | used under specific conditions in the last syllable of words, see § 20. |
| | ꜥ | forearm | a guttural sound unknown to English | corresponds to Hebrew ע *ʿayin*, Arabic ع *ʿain.* |
| | w | quail chick | *w* | |
| | b | foot | *b* | |
| | p | stool | *p* | |
| | f | horned viper | *f* | |
| | m | owl | *m* | |
| | n | water | *n* | corresponds to Hebrew נ *nūn*, but also to Hebrew ל *lāmedh.* |
| | r | mouth | *r* | corresponds to Hebrew ר *rēsh*, more rarely to Hebrew ל *lāmedh.* |
| | h | reed shelter in fields | *h* as in English | corresponds to Hebrew ה *hē*, Arabic ه *hā.* |
| | ḥ | wick of twisted flax | emphatic *h* | corresponds to Arabic ح *ḥā.* |
| | ḫ | placenta (?) | like *ch* in Scotch *loch* | corresponds to Arabic خ *ḫā.* |

(The Alphabet is continued on the next page.)

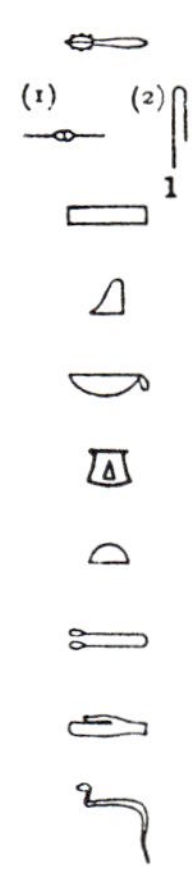

| | | | |
|---|---|---|---|
| ẖ | animal's belly with teats | perhaps like *ch* in German *ich* | interchanging early with [sign] *š*, later with [sign] *ḫ*, in certain words. |
| s | (1) bolt<br>(2) folded cloth | *s* | originally two separate sounds: (1) *z*, much like our *z*; (2) *ś*, unvoiced *s*. |
| š | pool | *sh* | early hardly different from [sign] *ẖ*. |
| ḳ | hill-slope | backward *k*; rather like our *q* in *queen* | corresponds to Hebrew ק *ḳōph*, Arabic ق *ḳāf*. |
| k | basket with handle | *k* | corresponds to Hebrew כ *kaph*, Arabic ك *kāf*. Written [sign] in hieratic. |
| g | stand for jar | hard *g* | |
| t | loaf | *t* | |
| ṯ | tethering rope | originally *tsh* (*č* or *tj*) | during Middle Kingdom persists in some words, in others is replaced by [sign] *t*. |
| d | hand | *d* | |
| ḏ | snake | originally *dj* and also a dull emphatic *s* (Hebrew צ) | during Middle Kingdom persists in some words, in others is replaced by [sign] *d*. |

OBS. Later alternative forms are [sign] for *w*, [sign] for *m*, [sign] for *n*, and [sign] for *t*. Of these, [sign] arose from an abbreviated form of [sign] in Middle Kingdom hieratic, so that it appears in our transcriptions of hieratic texts belonging to a time when [sign] was not yet written in hieroglyphic;[2] [sign] and [sign] originate in the biliteral signs for *ỉm*[3] and *tỉ* respectively, while [sign] is taken from the word *nt* 'crown of Lower Egypt'.[4] Note also that [sign] is used for *g* in a few old words.

[1] The form [sign] usually employed in printed books is not found on the monuments until a quite late period; early detailed forms are [sign] and [sign]. [2] *ÄZ.* 29, 47. [3] As *m* not before Tuthmosis I, *ÄZ.* 35, 170. [4] Already sporadically as *n* from early XII Dyn., ex. PETRIE, *Gizeh and Rifeh* 13 *g*.

Fig. I.5 The Egyptian alphabet, i.e. glyphs representing single consonants. Copied from Gardiner, *Egyptian Grammar*, p. 27, with the permission of its publisher, the Griffith Institute. See my Index of Egyptian Words for the alphabetical glyphs produced by the computer program Fontrix, and used in the index as headings.

| | | | |
|---|---|---|---|
| (F 40) 3w | (G 40) p3 | (M 16) h3 | (F 29) st |
| (U 23) 3b, mr | (O 1) pr | (N 41) hm | (M 8) s3 |
| (. .) jw | (F 22) ph | (M 2) hn | (H 6) sw |
| (Aa 13, .n, gs | (U 1) m3 | (D 2) hr | (V 7) sn |
| (Z 11) jm | (W 19) mj | (W 14) hs | (V 6) ss |
| (K 1) jn | (Y 5) mn | (T 2) hd | (Aa 28) kd |
| (D 4) jr | (N 36) mr | (M 12) h3 | (D 28) k3 |
| (M 40) js | (U 6) mr | (N 28) hc | (I 6) km |
| (O 29) c3 | (V 12) nh | (M 3) ht | (G 28) gm |
| (V 4) w3 | (F 31) ms | (K 4) h3 | (U 30) t3 |
| (T 21) wc | (D 52) mt | (D 33) hn | (U 33) tj |
| (F 13) wp | (W 24) nw | (F 26) hn | (U 15) tm |
| (E 34) wn | (U 19) nw | (T 28) hr | (G 47) t3 |
| (M 42) wn | (V 30) nb | (G 38) s3 | (U 28) d3 |
| (G 36) wr | (T 34) nm | (Aa 17/18) s3 | (N 26) dw |
| (V 24) wd | (F 20) ns | (M 23) sw | (M 36) dr |
| (G 29) b3 | (Aa 27) nd | (T 22) sn | Also: |
| (F 18) bh, hw | (E 23) rw | (V 29) sk, w3h | (M 22) nn |

Fig. I.6 Some biliteral signs. Taken from H. Brunner, *An Outline of Middle Egyptian Grammar*, p. 9, with the permission of Akademische Druck-u. Verlagsanstalt, Graz, Austria. The designations in parentheses are the sign numbers used by Gardiner in his *Egyptian Grammar*. Gardiner's sign list includes not only the classical alphabetical and biliteral signs depicted here and in Fig. I.5 but also the full range of signs used for determinatives and for other biliteral, triliteral, and quadriliteral words current in the Middle Kingdom.

(a)

(b)

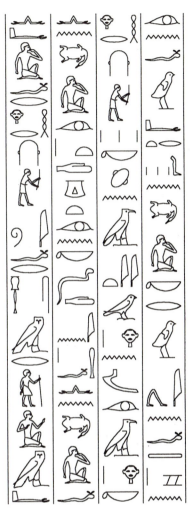

Fig. I.7 Three forms of an extract from "The Story of Sinuhe" prepared with the versatile and elegant computer program GLYPH written by Jan Buurman and Ed de Moel: (a) in the normal Egyptian writing from right to left (here justified on the right and left), (b) in reverse writing from left to right (here justified only on the left), and (c) in normal columnar writing (with the columns justified at top and bottom and to be read from right to left). It is an ideal program for preparing blocks of texts but cannot yet easily embed glyphs into a sophisticated word-processing program. Notice how glyphs are grouped together on the same and differing levels and face the direction from which the writing begins. These specimens were printed on a Kyocera Laser printer (F-1000A).

(c)

Fig. 1.8   The Palette of Narmer, recto and verso. Predynastic or Dynasty 1. Cairo Museum.

-750-

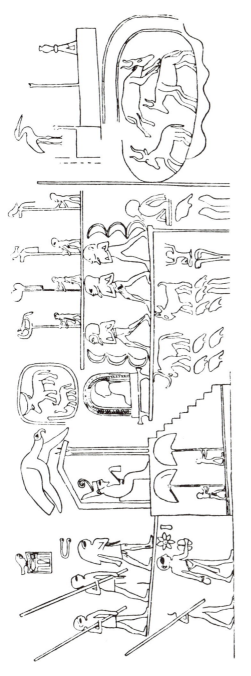

Fig. I.9   The Narmer Mace-Head. According to Quibell, *Hierakonpolis*, Vol. 1, pl. XXVI.B.

I            I
IO          ∩
IOO         ↷
I,OOO       ⚱

IO,OOO
IOO,OOO
I,OOO,OOO

Fig. I.10   Egyptian signs for the powers of 10.

-751-

Fig. I.11a  Two statues of Khasekhem from Hieraconpolis. Dynasty 2. The left one in the Ashmolean Museum at Oxford and the
right one from the Cairo Museum.

Fig. I.11b  Details from the bases of the above statues giving the number of victims. In each, the
Horus name of the King as appearing on the top side of the pedestal is given. See Quibell, *Hierakonpolis,* pl. LX.

Fig. I.12   A predynastic sealing with signs for water *(mw)* according to Emery, *Hor-Aha,* p. 33.

Fig. I.13   Stela of the Horus Djet. Dynasty 1. Louvre Museum. Photograph by Sue Clagett.

Fig. I.14b  Stela of Queen Meryetneith. Dynasty 1. Cairo Museum.
Photograph by M. Clagett.

Fig. I.14a  Stela of the Horus Nebre. Dynasty 2. The Metropolitan
Museum of Art. Photograph by Sue Clagett.

-754-

Fig. I.15a  A supposed sealing of Menes (restored). Dynasty 1. Copied from Gardiner, *Egypt of the Pharaohs,* p. 405, with the permission of the Oxford University Press.

Fig. I.15b  A Tablet from Naqada. Dynasty 1. From Gardiner, *ibid.*, with the permission of the Oxford University Press.

Fig. I.16  A wooden label from Abydos. Dynasty 1. Drawn after Petrie, *Royal Tombs,* Vol. 2, pl. X,2.

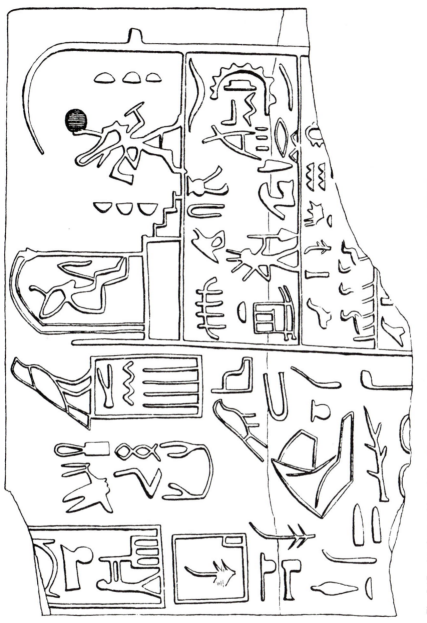

Fig. I.17   An ebony tablet of King Den. Dynasty 1. After Petrie, *Royal Tombs*, Vol. 1, pl. XV,16.

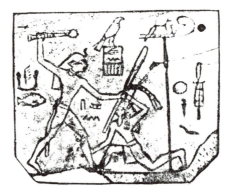

Fig. I.18a  An ivory label of King Den in the
British Museum. Dynasty 1.

Fig. I.18b  An ivory label of King Semerkhet. Dynasty 1. After
Petrie, *Royal Tombs*, Vol. 1, pl. XVII,26.

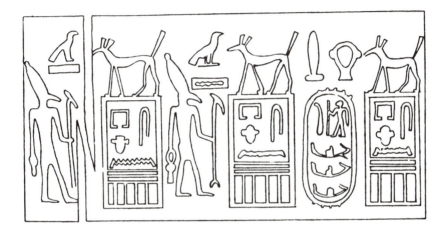

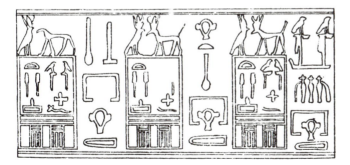

Fig. I.19a   A group of four sealings, the two above found in the Metropolitan Museum, and the two below taken from Petrie, *Royal Tombs,* Vol. 2, pls. XXII,179 and XXIII,197.

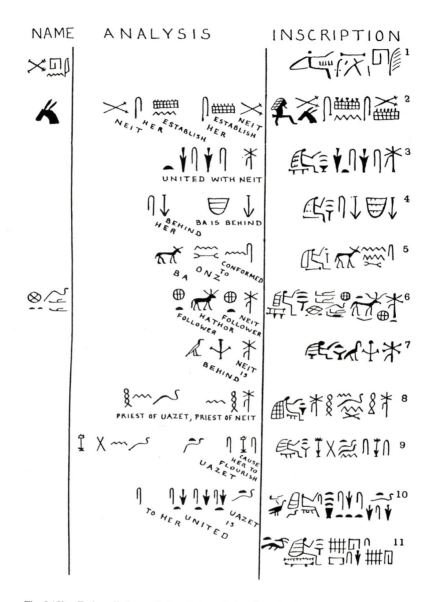

Fig. I.19b   Early cylinders with inscriptions. Taken from Petrie, "The Earliest Inscriptions," p. 65.

Fig. I.20 Sketches of stelas near the first-dynasty, royal tombs at Abydos. From Petrie, *Royal Tombs*, Vol. 1, pl. XXXI.

Fig. I.22  Archaic stela from Helwan. Reproduced from Vandier, *Manuel d'archéologie égyptienne*, Vol. 1, p. 733, with the permission of A. et J. Picard, Paris.

Fig. I.21  Stela of Sabef from Abydos, End of Dynasty 1. Cairo Museum. Photograph by M. Clagett.

Fig. I.23 Stela of the nobleman Merka. End of
Dynasty 1. Reproduced from Emery, *Archaic Egypt*,
pl. 30a, with the permission of Penguin Books Ltd.

Fig. I.24a   Stone stela of a princess from a tomb niche in Saqqara. Dynasty 2.

Fig. I.24b   Another stone stela from Saqqara (painted). Dynasty 2.

Fig. I.25  Stela of Tetenankh. Dynasty 3. Drawing
from Vandier, *Manuel,* Vol. 1, p. 754. Copied with
the permission of A. et J. Picard, Paris.

Fig. I.26  Slab-stela of Prince Wepemnofret from his Giza tomb. Dynasty 4. Copied with the
permission of the Lowie Museum of Anthropology, University of California at Berkeley, from
Fazzini, *Images for Eternity,* p. 28.

Fig. I.27   Reliefs in an offering-niche of the
tomb of Khabawsekar at Saqqara. Dynasty
3. Cairo Museum.

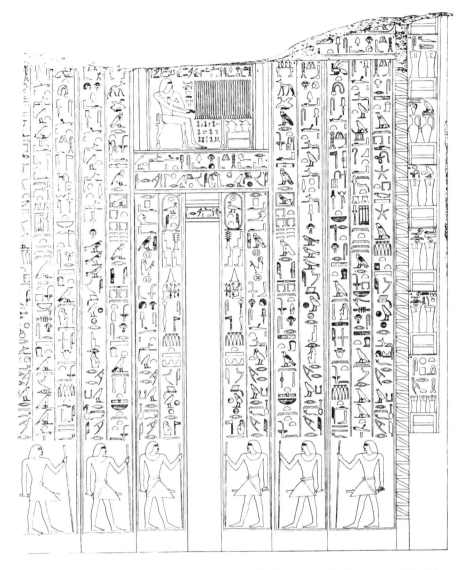

Fig. I.28 Drawing of a false door from the west wall of chamber A8 of the tomb of Mereruka, Saqqara. Dynasty 6. According to Oriental Institute of the University of Chicago, *The Mastaba of Mereruka*, Part I, pl. 62. Courtesy of The Oriental Institute of the University of Chicago.

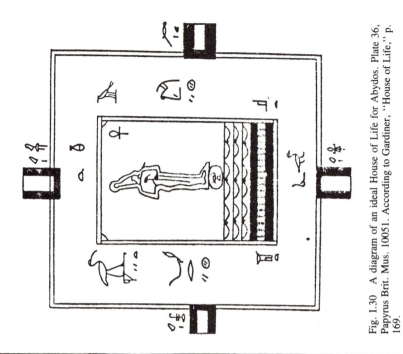

Fig. I.30 A diagram of an ideal House of Life for Abydos. Plate 36, Papyrus Brit. Mus. 10051. According to Gardiner, "House of Life," p. 169.

Fig. I.29 A list of the names of some scribes on a slab from Dynasty 3, now at the Ashmolean Museum. Cf. Garstang, *Tombs of the Third Egyptian Dynasty*, pl. XXVII,2.

Fig. I.31a   Seshat on a limestone relief from the mortuary temple of Sesostris I at Lisht (Dynasty XII).
Photograph provided through the courtesy of The Brooklyn Museum, Charles Edwin Wilbour Fund.

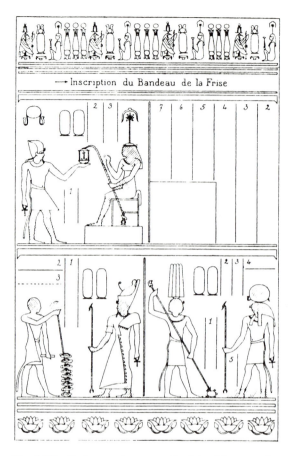

Inscription du Bandeau de la Frise

Fig. I.31b   Seshat on the east wall of the Library at the Temple of Edfu. According to Chassinat, *Le Temple d'Edfou*, Vol. 3, pl. LXXXII.

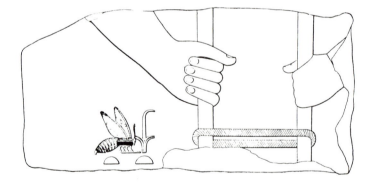

Fig. I.31c   The hands of a king and a divinity (Seshat?), stretching the chord, from a block at Khatâᶜna. Most likely Dynasty 12. Taken from Habachi, "Khatâᶜna," pl. VII.

Fig. I.32   The Palermo Stone, recto. H. Schäfer, "Ein Bruchstüch," Tafel I.

-771-

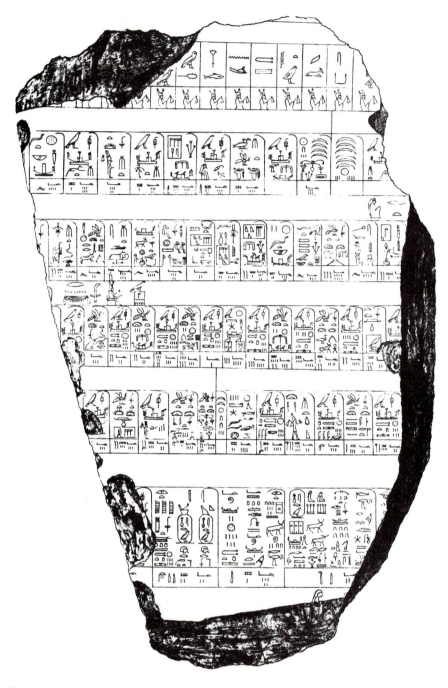

Fig. I.33  The Palermo Stone, recto. Drawing according to Pellegrini, ''Nota sopra un'inscrizione,''
Tavola I.

Fig. I.34 The Palermo Stone, verso. Schäfer, Taf. II.

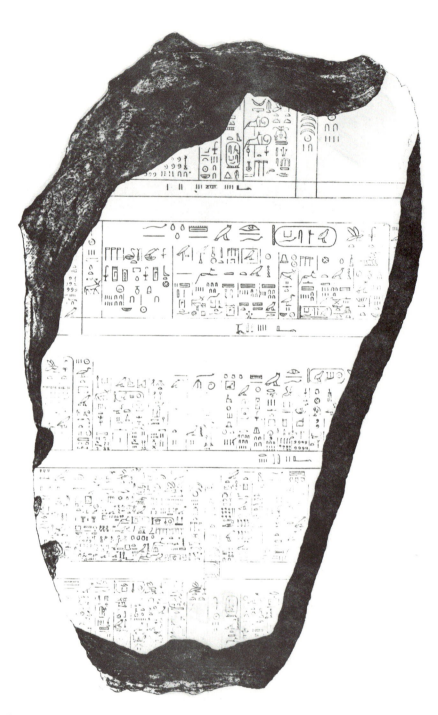

Fig. I.35  Palermo Stone verso. Pellegrini, Tav. II.

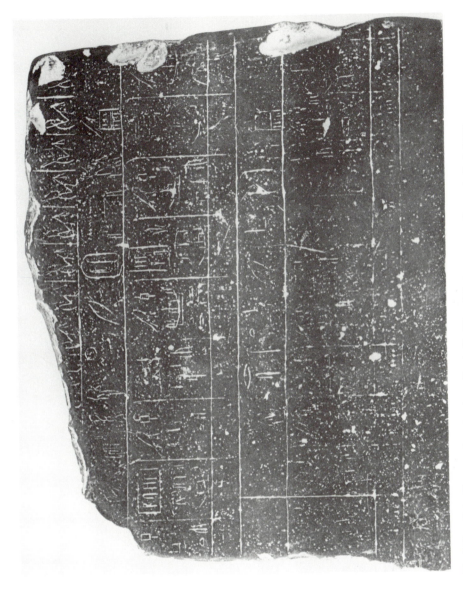

Fig. I.36a   Cairo Fragment 1, recto. According to Gauthier, "Quatre nouveaux fragments." pl. XXV.

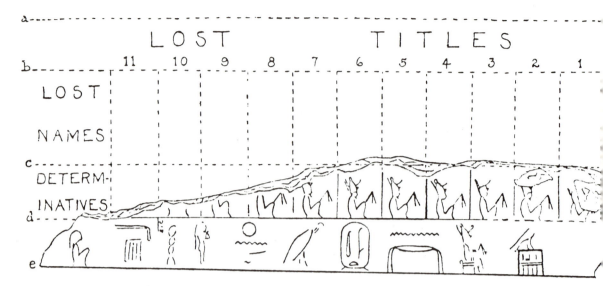

Fig. I.36b   Top lines of Cairo Fragment 1, recto. Drawn according to Breasted, "The predynastic union," pl. I.

Fig. I.37   Cairo Fragment 1, verso (significant detail). Gauthier, pl. XXVII.

Fig. I.38   Cairo Fragments 2 and 3. Gauthier, pl. XXX.

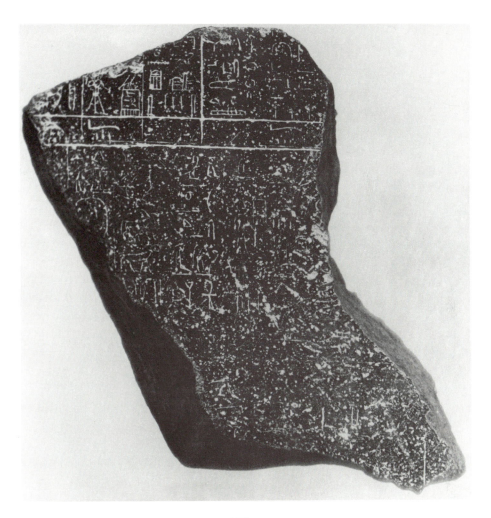

Fig. I.39   Cairo Fragment 4. Gauthier, pl. XXXI.

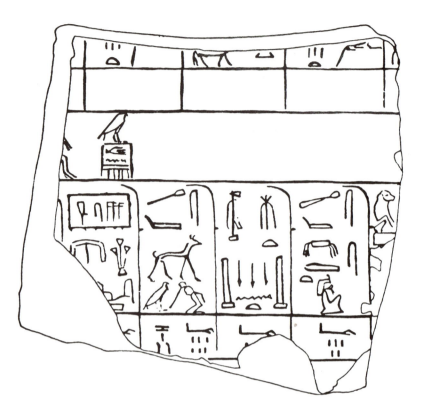

Fig. I.40  Cairo Fragment 5. Taken from de Cenival, "Un nouveau fragment," p. 15.

Fig. I.41a and b    London Fragment, recto and verso. Photographs provided
by the Petrie Collection of University College, London University.

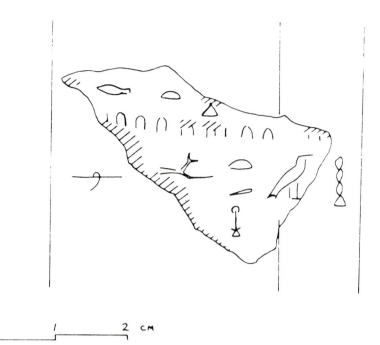

0    1    2 CM

Fig. I.41c    London Fragment, verso. Drawing by Reeves, "A Fragment of Fifth Dynasty Annals," p. 50.

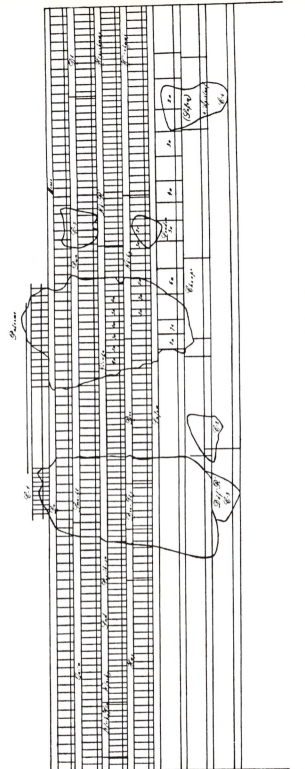

Fig. I.42 Early Annals, recto, showing the location of the fragments. Redrawn according to Helck, "Bemerkungen zum Annalenstein," p. 34. The Fragments are labeled Palermo, C-1 to C-5 (Cairo), and London.

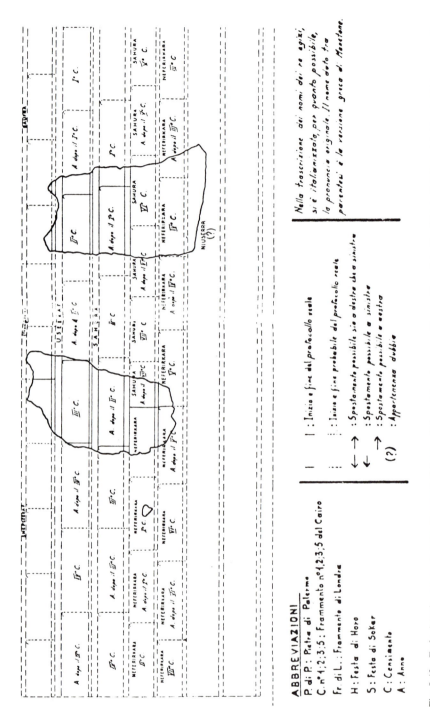

Fig. I.43   Early Annals, verso, showing Fragments Palermo, C-1, and London, according to Giustolisi, ''La 'Pietra di Palermo','' March 1969, pp. 46–47.

A fragment of the Turin Canon of Kings.

Part of the Table of Abydos.

Part of the Table of Saḳḳâra.

Fig. I.44a   Samples of three principal king-lists. Copied from Gardiner, *Egypt of the Pharaohs*, p. 49, with the permission of the Oxford University Press.

-785-

Fig. I.44b and c   Parts of the king-list from the temple of Seti I at Abydos. Taken from Capart's *Memphis*, pp. 115, 146.

Fig. I.45   An inscription of Horus Djer on a
stone vessel. Dynasty I. Taken from Borchardt,
*Die Annalen*, p. 31.

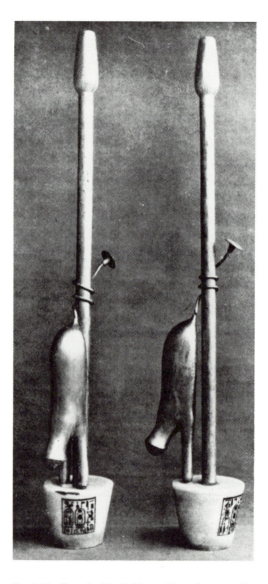

Fig. I.46  Two Anubis Emblems. The pelt on a staff,
read as "He who is in the bandaging room." Taken
from Carter, *Tut-ankh-Amen*. Vol. 2, opposite p. 34.

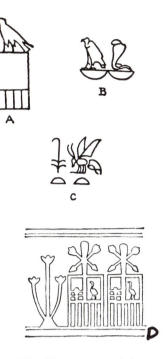

Fig. I.47a  The Archaic period. A-C reproduced from Emery, *Archaic Egypt,* Fig. 69, p. 107, and D from *ibid.,* Fig. 8, p. 49, with the permission of Penguin Books Ltd.

Fig. I.47b  A relief in the Metropolitan Museum of Art from Dynasty 3, showing the titles: "King of Upper and Lower Egypt" (i.e. He of the Sedge and the Bee) and "He of the Two Ladies" (i.e. the *nebty*: the Vulture-goddess Nekhbet of Upper Egypt and the Cobra-goddess Wadjet of Lower Egypt).

Fig. I.47c  The early use of the cartouche around Sneferu's name, but without a "Son of Re" name or title. Dynasty 4. Relief of the Personalized Estates from the Valley temple of the Bent Pyramid in Dashur.

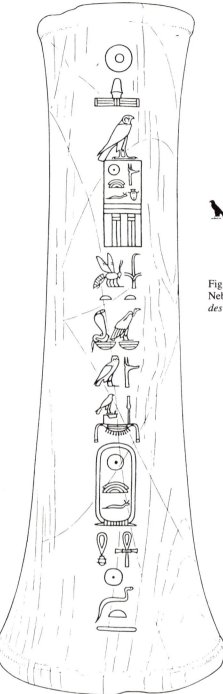

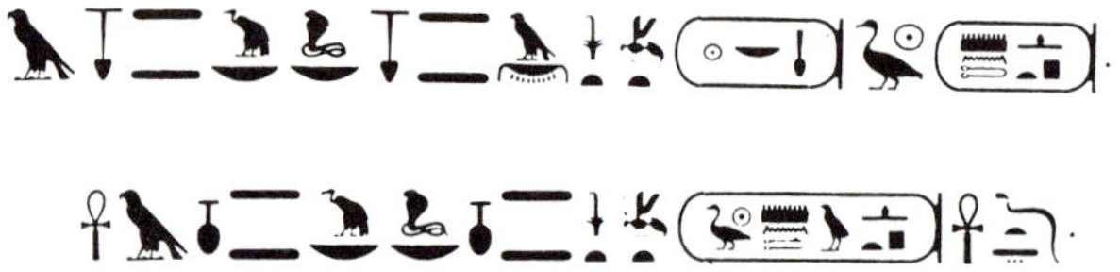

Fig. I.47e   An inscription from Aswan giving the full titulary of Nebhepetre Mentuhotep. Dynasty 11. Taken from Gauthier, *Le Livre des rois*, Vol. 1, p. 229. Notice that all five titles are now used.

Fig. I.47d   A drawing of a diorite stand with the names and titles of Chephren, but without the "Son of Re" title. Dynasty IV. In the Metropolitan Museum of Art.

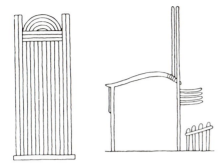

Fig. I.48 The Dual Shrines. The figure on the left represents the Per-nw of Lower Egypt at Buto and that on the right the Per-wer of Upper Egypt at Hieraconpolis. The drawings are those of Frankfort, *Kingship and the Gods*, Fig. 30 after p. 212. Copied with the permission of the University of Chicago Press.

# PROBLEM 48

Fig. I.49 Problem 48 of the Rhind Mathematical Papyrus. From Chace, *The Rhind Mathematical Papyrus*, Vol. 2, pl. 70.

| | Cubit-Areas ( ⌐ ) | Avouras ( – ℓ – ◦◦ ) |
|---|---|---|
| ḫꜣ ( ℧ ) | 1000 | 10 |
| sṯꜣt ( ⌐ ᵃ ◦◦ ᵃ ⌐ ) | 100 | 1* |
| rmn ( ◢ ) | 50 | 1/2 |
| ḥsb ( X ) | 25 | 1/4 |
| sꜣ ( ⨯ ) | 12-1/2 | 1/8 |
| mḥ ( ⌐ ) | 1 | 1/100 |

*1 aroura (or sṯꜣt) = 2728.7 sq. meters

Fig. I.50   Area measurements on the Palermo Stone.

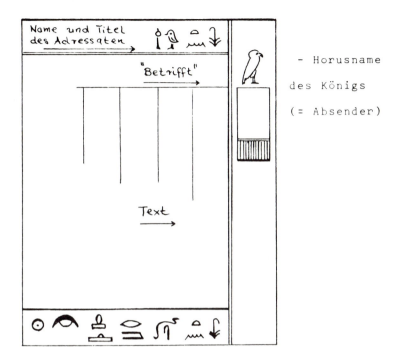

Fig. I.51   The form of a royal, written command in the Old Kingdom. Taken from Gödecken, *Eine Betrachtung*, p. 3, with the kind permission of Verlag Otto Harrassowitz.

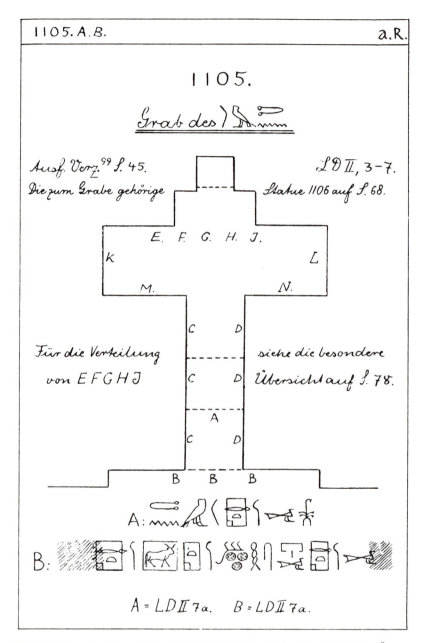

Fig. I.52  Location of inscriptions in the tomb of Metjen. Taken from H. Schäfer, *Ägyptische Inschriften*, as are the hieroglyphic transcriptions here and in the remaining figures. The photographs of Inscriptions A and B on the next page and those of the remaining inscriptions in the succeeding figures are reproduced from the plates appended to Goedicke, "Die Laufbahn des *Mtn*," with the author's kind permission. The references to LD are to Lepsius' *Denkmäler*.

Inscription A.

Inscription B.

C.

Vielleicht ist die Inschrift C an D anzuschliessen. C = LD II, 6 und 7ª.

Fig. I.53   Inscription C.

Drei Frauen als Vertreterinnen von Dörfern

Die oberste bezeichnet als [hieroglyphs] so!

die beiden unteren ohne Bezeichnung.

a. So! Ein [hat wohl nie da-
gekandem.]

D. (Forts.)

11.

10.

9.

8.

7.

6.

5.

4.

3.

2.

1.

D.

D = LD II 5 und 75.

Fig. I.54  Inscription D.

E—I.

*Übersicht:*

E.

F.

I  II

J.

iii

G

H.

E-I = LD.II,3.

E.

1.
2.
3.
4.
5.
6.
7.
8.
9.

E. (Forts.)

10.
11.
12.
13.
14.

E. (Forts.)

15.
16.
17.
18.

Fig. I.55    Arrangement of Inscriptions E-I. Inscription E.

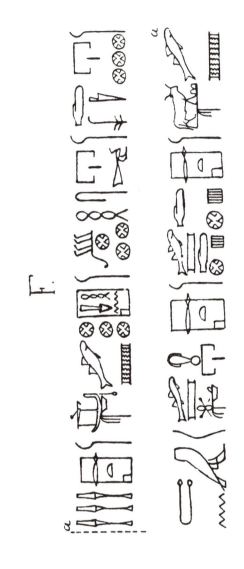

F.

Fig. I.56 Inscription F.

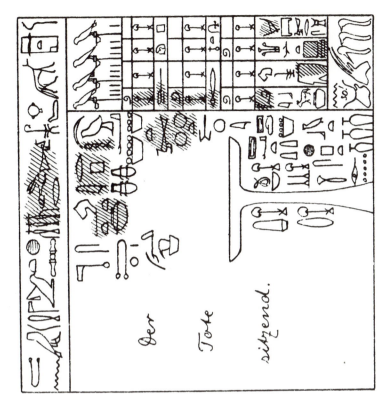

der

Tote

sitzend.

G (Fonts.)

III.

IV.

VI.

I.

(See page 805 for photographs.)

-803-

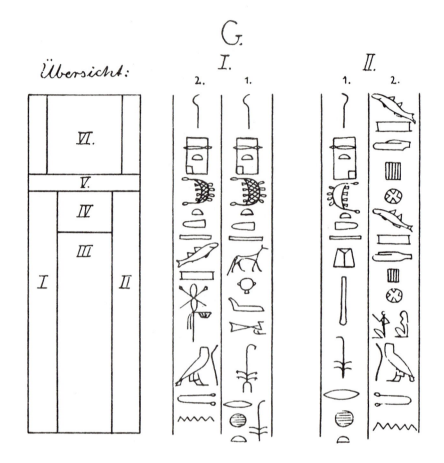

Fig. I.57   Inscriptions G I-II, IV-VI.

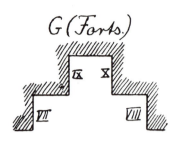

## G (Forts.)

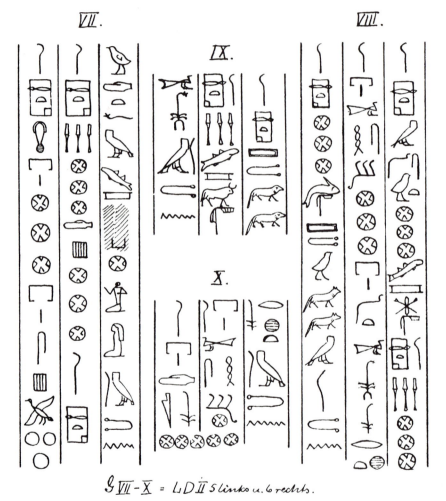

*G VII – X = L D II 5 links u. 6 rechts.*

Fig. I.58   Inscriptions G III, VII-VIII, X.

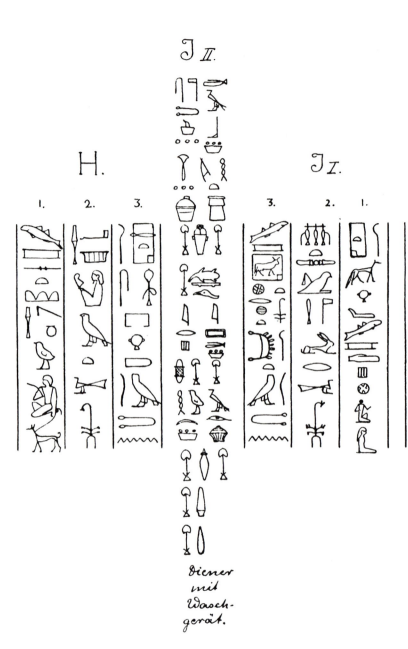

Diener
mit
Wasch-
gerät.

Inschrift J

Inschrift H

Fig. I.59  Inscriptions H and J.

Unten: Der Verstorbene stehend nach l. Vor ihm zwei Männer mit gefangenen Antilopen (die Darstellung schliesst an
K an. Über ihm:

Mitte: 4 Männer mit Gaben, nach r. Über ihnen:

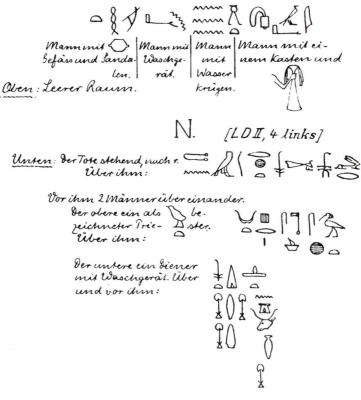

| Mann mit Gefäss und Sanda- len. | Mann mit Waschge- rät. | Mann mit Wasser krügen. | Mann mit ei- nem Kasten und |
|---|---|---|---|

Oben: Leerer Raum.

Unten: der Tote stehend, nach r.
    Über ihm:

Vor ihm 2 Männer über einander.
   Der obere ein als
   zeichneter Trie- be-
   ster. Über ihm:

   Der untere ein Diener
   mit Waschgerät. Über
   und vor ihm:

Mitte: 4 Männer mit Gaben, nach links. Über ihnen:

| Mann mit einem Futteral. | Mann mit Stab, Sandalen und Halsband(?) | Mann mit Se- stell der Form | Mann mit Ge- fäss und mit Kopfstütze. |
|---|---|---|---|

Oben : 4 Männer beim Schlachten eines Rindes 5. 4. 3. 2. 1
No 1. aufseher. No 3 schneidet. No 2 und 4 ziehen an den
Beinen des Rindes. No 5 trägt eine Schale mit Herz und
          Beischriften:      Rippen fort.

No 3. ohne
Beischrift.     zu No 2.     zu No 1.

Zu No 5 und 4          zum Rind.

Kultkammer des *Mṯn*: Inschrift M

Fig. I.60   Inscriptions M and N.

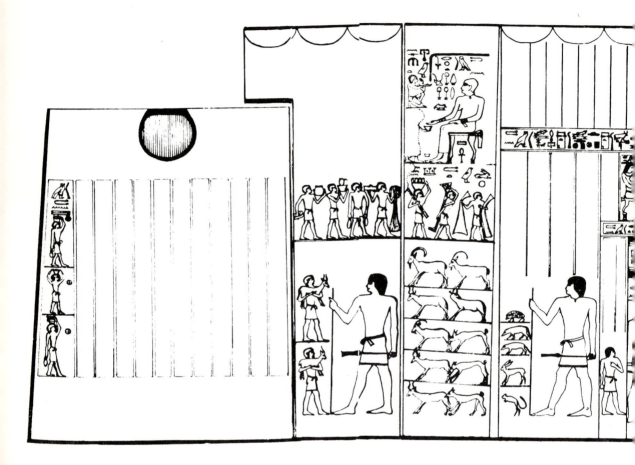

Fig. I.61   The backwall of Metjen's Cult-Chamber. Taken from Gödecken, *Eine Betrachtung*, Abbildung I after p. 168, with the kind permission of Verlag Otto Harrassowitz.

ABBILDUNG I

DIE KULTKAMMER
DES MTN

Fig. I.62 Relief from a tomb wall at Saqqara. Dynasty 19. It pictures famous men, among whom in the top row are the sages Imhotep and Kaires, while in the bottom row there are more sages, including Khety and Khakheperreseneb. Reproduced from Simpson, *The Literature of Ancient Egypt,* Fig. 6, with permission of the Yale University Press.

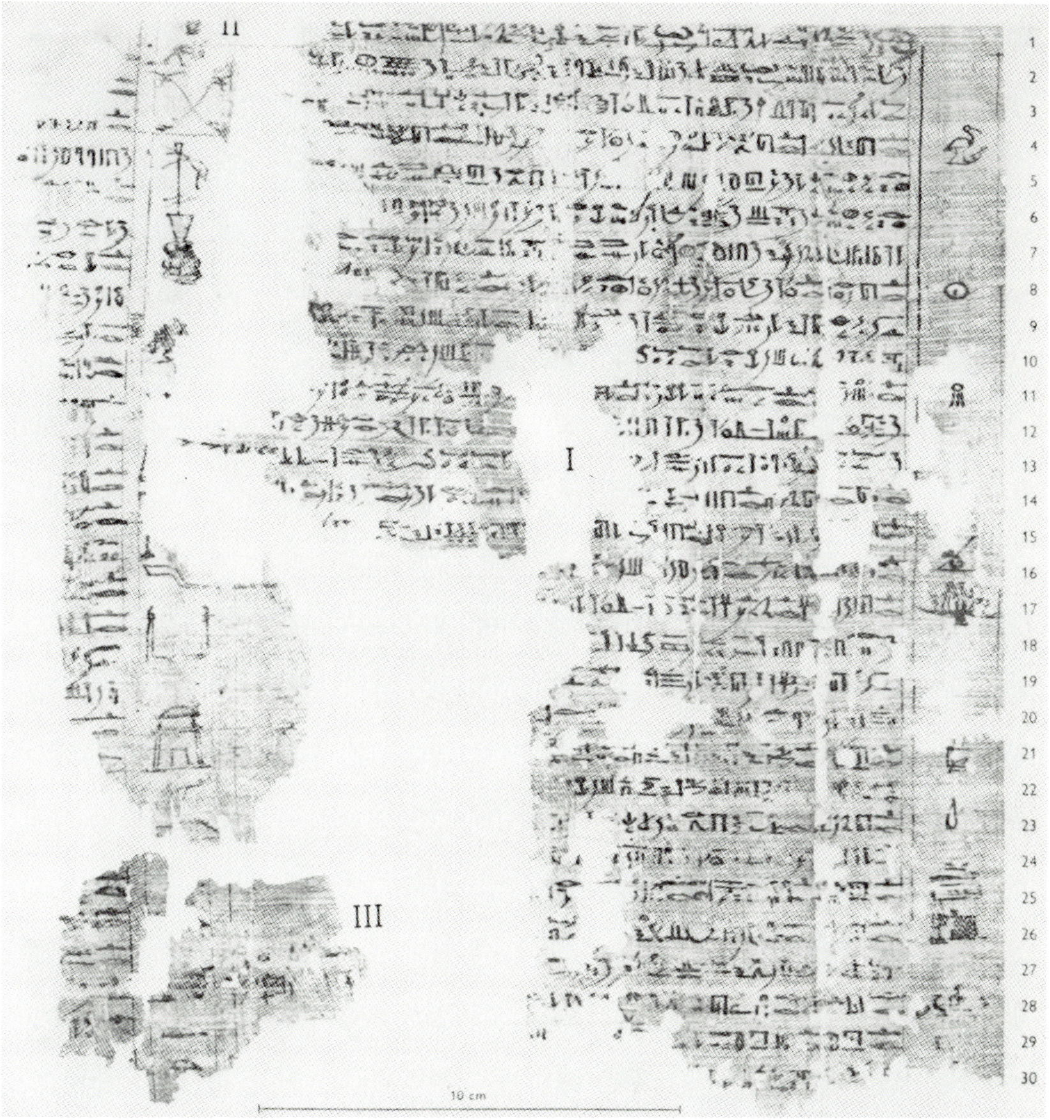

Fig. I.63   Fragments from a hieroglyphic dictionary. Taken from Iversen, *Papyrus Carlsberg Nr. VII*, following p. 31.

Fig. II.1   The rebirth of the sun as the Khepri beetle.
Schematized drawing from a papyrus in the British Mu-
seum. Cf. E.A.W. Budge, *The Gods of the Egyptians,*
Vol. 1 (Chicago and London, 1904), p. 204.

Fig. II.2a   Nut as the Divine or Celestial Cow. A watercolor by Robert Hay in the British Library (Add. Mss. 29820, f. 97), reproduced in E. Hornung, *Der ägyptische Mythos von der Himmelskuh (Orbis biblicus et orientalis,* Vol. 42), Fribourg, Switzerland, Abb. 2. Copied with the permission of the Éditions Universitaires, Fribourg, Suisse.

Fig. II.2b   Nut as the sky being supported
by Shu (or Maat?), with Geb as the earth
below. Taken from Erman, *A Handbook of
Egyptian Religion*, p. 29.

Fig. II.2c   Nut from the Tomb of Ramesses II. After Piankoff,
*The Tomb of Ramesses VI*, Vol. 1, Facsimile facing page 33. Reproduced with the permission of Princeton University Press.

Fig. II.3   An Ivory comb with the name of the Horus
Wadji. Dynasty 1. In the Cairo Museum. Copied from
Frankfort, *Kingship and the Gods*, Fig. 17, with the per-
mission of the University of Chicago Press.

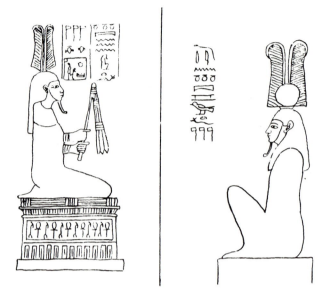

Fig. II.4   Nun in human form and called "Father of the Gods."
According to Lanzone, *Dizionario di mitologia,* Tav. CLXVI.

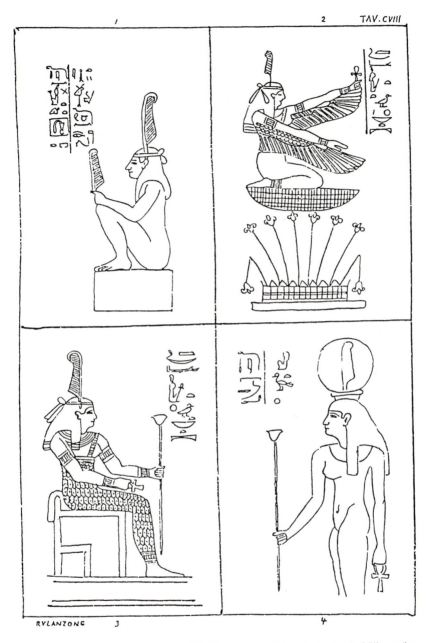

Fig. II.5  Several depictions of Maat, Daughter of Re, Mistress in the Land of Silence (i.e. the Otherworld), reproduced by Lanzone, *Dizionario di mitologia*, Tav. CVIII.

Fig. II.6a "The Provider of Attributes." Double-headed cosmic snake. Copied from Clark, *Myth and Symbol in Ancient Egypt,* Fig. 7, p. 52, with the permission of Thames and Hudson Ltd.

Fig. II.6b The sun-god as a child enclosed in the snake with his tail in his mouth, the Ouroboros. Mortuary Papyrus of Hirweben A. Cairo Museum. Dynasty 21. Reproduced from Hornung, *Conceptions of God in Ancient Egypt,* p. 164.

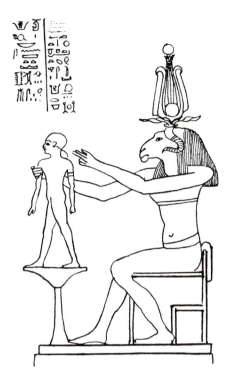

Fig. II.7   Khnum modeling man on his potter's
wheel. According to Lanzone, *Dizionario di mitologia,* Tav. CCCXXXVI,3.

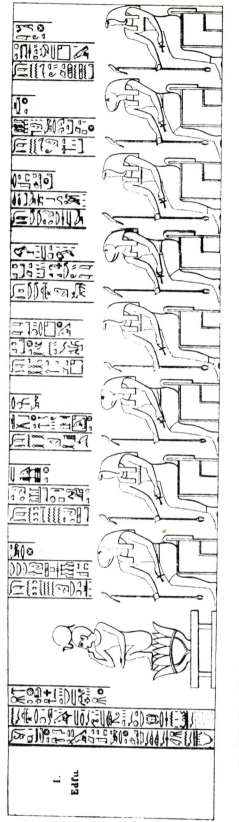

Fig. II.8  The eight chaos-gods depicted as watching the young sun-god rising from the Lotus flower. The male gods have rearing cobras for heads. Taken from Lepsius, *Über die Götter der vier Elemente*, Taf. I.

Fig. II.9  Thoth as an Ibis facing a small figure of Maat. Dynasty 26. Kestner Museum, Hannover.

Fig. II.10  Amon-Re-Atum, the Ibis-headed Thoth, and Seshat writing King Ramesses II's titulary on the leaves of the Sacred Tree. Reproduced from Erman, *Life in Ancient Egypt,* p. 347.

Fig. II.11   The Emergence of the young sun-god from a lotus blossom on the primeval hill of Hermopolis. Saitic period. Pelizaeus Museum at Hildesheim (nr. 60-Bronze).

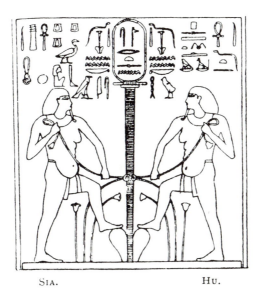

SIA.                              HU.

Fig. II.12a  Hu and Sia as Nile-gods tying the South
and the North together. Reproduced from Gautier and
Jéquier, *Fouilles de Licht*, p. 34.

Fig. II.12b  The bark of Re with Sia (the second anthropomorphic figure) and Hu (the
eighth), their names appearing above them. Reproduced by Jéquier from the *Book of Amduat*
in his *Considérations sur les religions égyptiennes*, p. 39, and copied with the permission
of Les Éditions de la Baconnière, Boudry, Suisse. In my figures from the *Amduat* given
below, the names are not included.

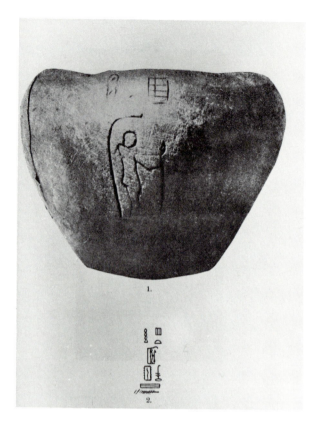

Fig. II.13  Two early representations of Ptah: the first on an al-
abaster bowl from Tarkhan dating from about Dynasty 1 and the
second from the Palermo Stone. See Sandman Holmberg, *The God
Ptah*, p. 65*.

Fig. II.14a  Ptah on the small shrine of Sesostris I at
Karnak. Here Ptah seems to be standing in an open chapel
as in early representations.

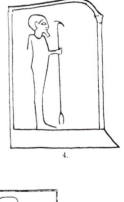

4.

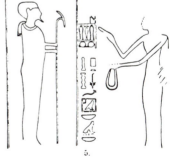

5.

Fig. II.14b  Two other Middle-Kingdom depictions of
Ptah, where he is in a closed chapel. See Sandman Holmberg, p. 67*.

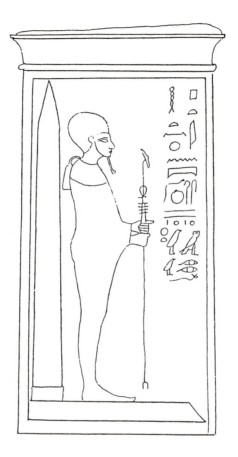

Fig. II.15   Another depiction of Ptah in a closed
chapel or naos, as reproduced by Lanzone, *Dizionario di mitologia,* Tav. XCII.

Fig. II.16   Relief from the shrine of Sesostris I at Karnak showing a very early representation of Amun in his ithyphallic form.

Fig. II.17   A predynastic palette in the form of a fish, with perhaps some religious significance. In the Lowie Museum of Anthropology. Copied from Fazzini, *Images for Eternity*, p. 12, with the permission of The Lowie Museum of Anthropology, The University of California at Berkeley.

Fig. II.18a   A predynastic vase with a ship bearing a standard of possible religious significance, in the Lowie Museum of Anthropology. Copied from Fazzini, p. 11, with the permission of The Lowie Museum of Anthropology, The University of California at Berkeley.

Fig. II.18b   A predynastic figure of a dog or jackal in the Lowie Museum. Copied from Fazzini, p. 14, with the permission of The Lowie Museum of Anthropology, The University of California at Berkeley.

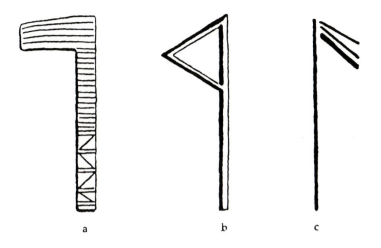

Fig. II.19a  Forms of the hieroglyph for "god" *(ntr)*, in reverse chronological order. From Hornung, *Conceptions of God*, p. 34.

Fig. II.19b  Other hieroglyphs for "god." From Hornung, *Conceptions of God*, p. 39.

Fig. II.20   Some figures of gods on early dynastic objects. From Hornung, *Conceptions of God*, p. 109.

Fig. II.21   Hathor from the tomb of Tuthmosis IV. Taken from Hornung, *Conceptions of God*, p. 111.

Fig. II.22  Hathor head in the Metropolitan Museum. Dynasty 30. Photograph by M. Clagett.

Fig. II.23  Royal family of Amarna: Akhenaten, Nefertiti, and daughters. With hands at the end of rays holding ankh-signs to the noses of the royal couple. It is in the style of the early Amarna period. Ägyptisches Museum, Berlin (West).

Fig. II.24   The "trio" of Amun, Mut, and Tutankhamen, with the king as the divine child between the gods. The facial similarity between father and son is evident. Cairo Museum.

Fig. II.25   A vignette for Spell 110 of the *Book of the Dead* (Papyr. Berlin No. 3008), depicting the Field of Rushes. Taken from Erman, *A Handbook of Egyptian Religion,* p. 92.

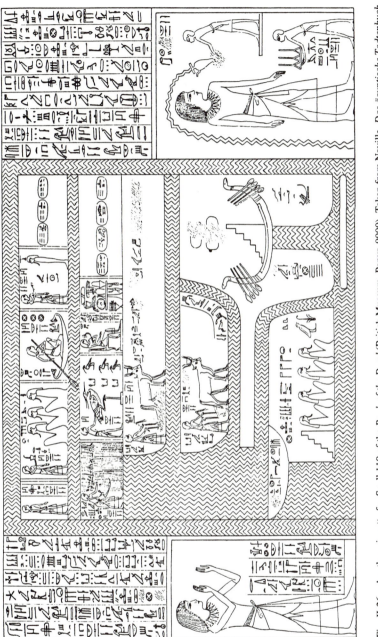

Fig. II.26   Another vignette for Spell 110 of the *Book of the Dead* (British Museum, Papyr. 9900). Taken from Naville, *Das ägyptische Todtenbuch.*
Vol. 1, p. CXXIII.

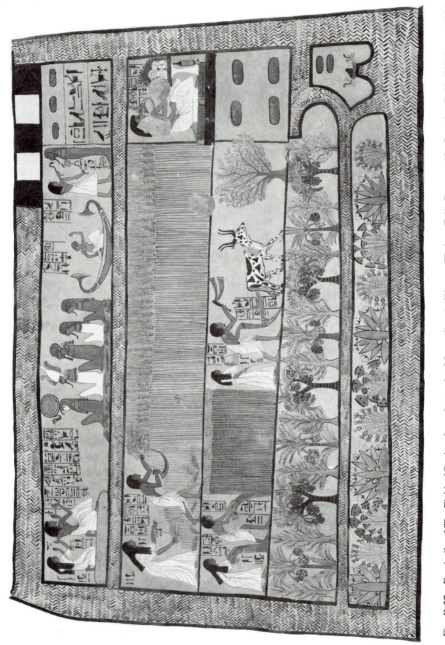

Fig. II.27 Facsimile of The Field of Rushes from the tomb of Sennedjem in Western Thebes (T 1). Dynasty 19. Copy by C. K. Wilkinson, 1922. Photograph supplied by The Metropolitan Museum of Art.

Fig. II.28 A plan showing the routes about which texts are displayed for the *Book of Two Ways*. It appears on a coffin from el-Barsha, now in the Cairo Museum (28083). Reproduced from de Buck, *The Egyptian Coffin Texts*, Vol. 7, Plan 1 (right side). Courtesy of the Oriental Institute of the University of Chicago.

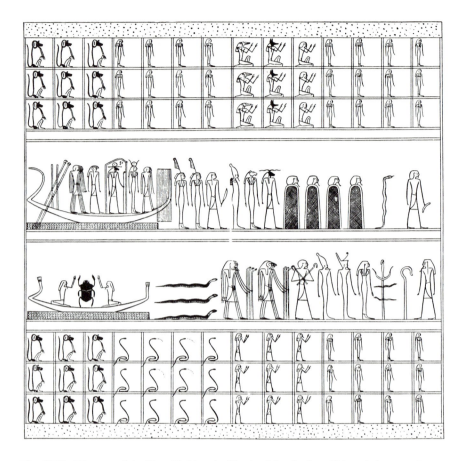

Fig. II.29   Diagram of the First Division (or Hour) of the *Amduat*. This and the next eleven diagrams (Figs. II.30-II.40) are taken from Piankoff, *The Tomb of Ramesses VI,* pp. 227–318, and reproduced with the permission of Princeton University Press. The texts that appear with these diagrams have been omitted from the diagrams but are translated partially in Doc. II.4.

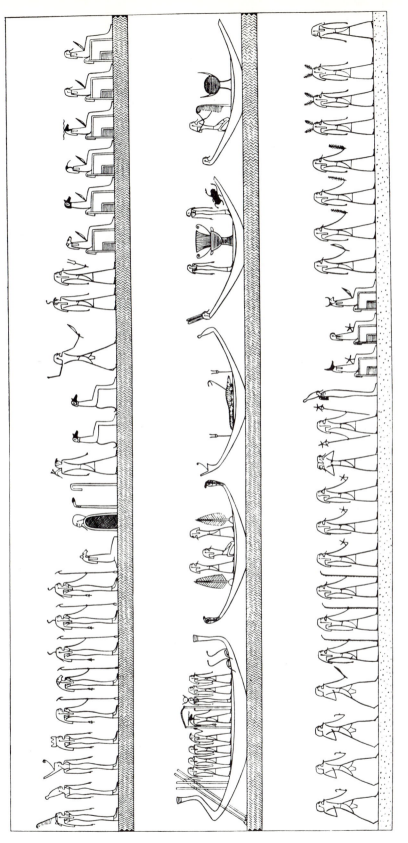

Fig. II.30  Diagram of the Second Division of the *Amduat*.

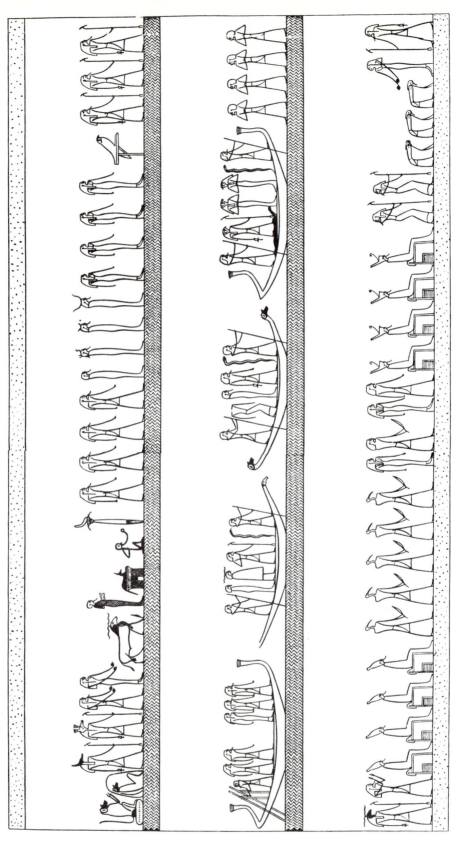

Fig. II.31   Diagram of the Third Division of the *Amduat*.

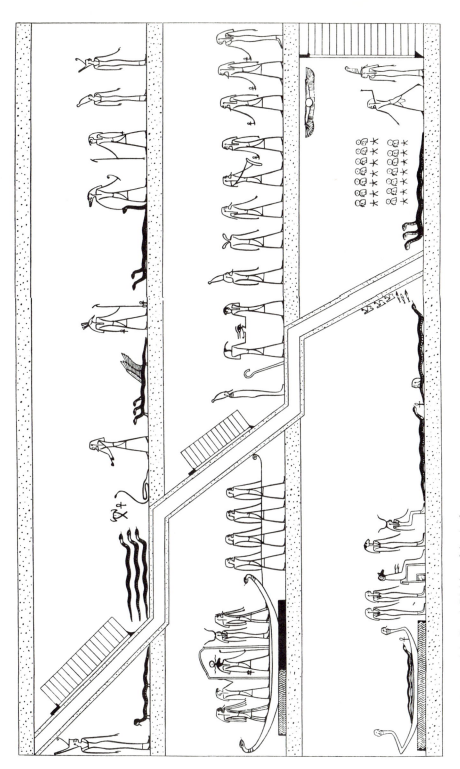

Fig. II.32   Diagram of the Fourth Division of the *Amduat*.

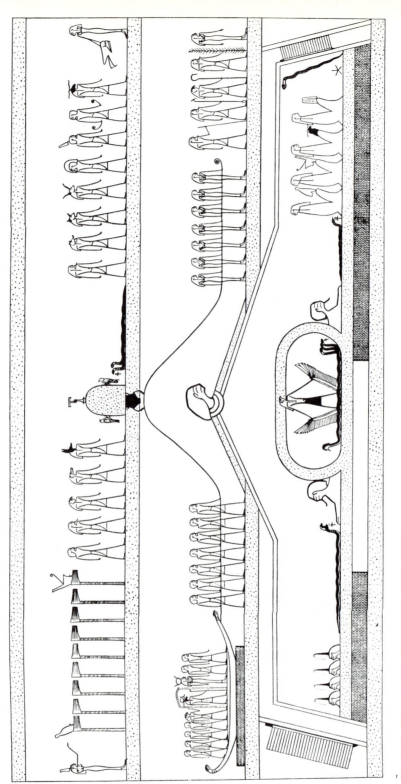

Fig. II.33   Diagram of the Fifth Division of the *Amduat*.

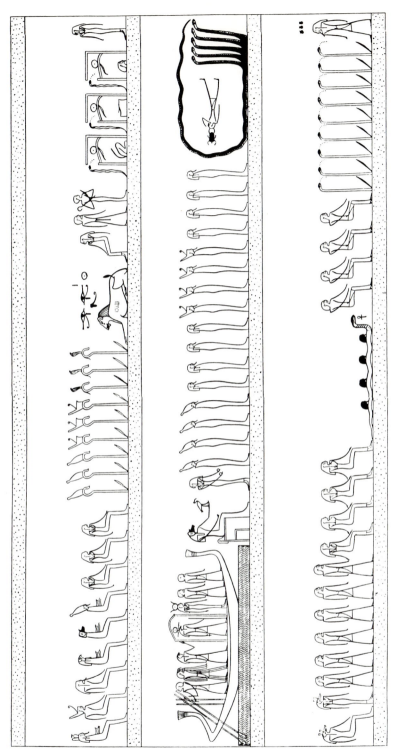

Fig. II.34  Diagram of the Sixth Division of the *Amduat*.

-845-

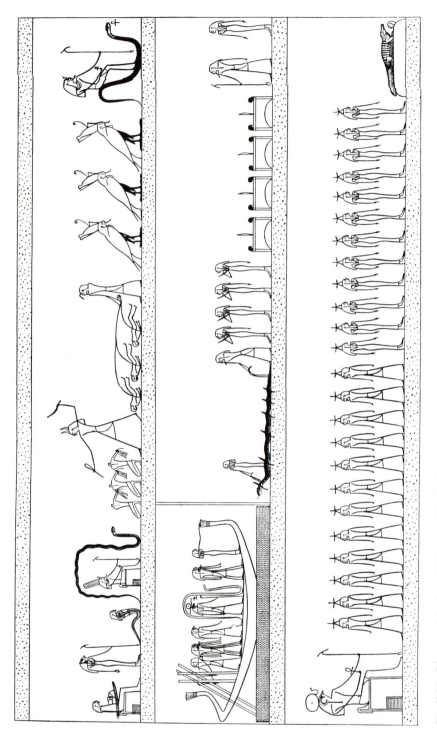

Fig. II.35  Diagram of the Seventh Division of the *Amduat*.

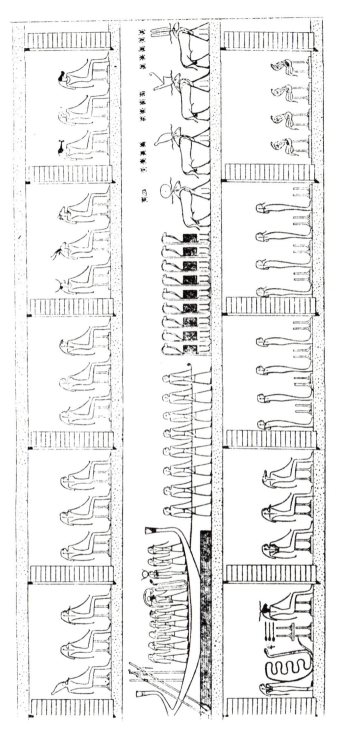

Fig. II.36  Diagram of the Eighth Division of the *Amduat*.

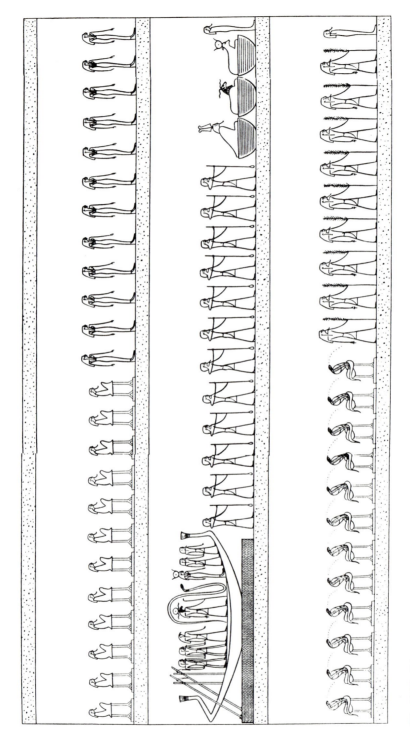

Fig. II.37 Diagram of the Ninth Division of the *Amduat*.

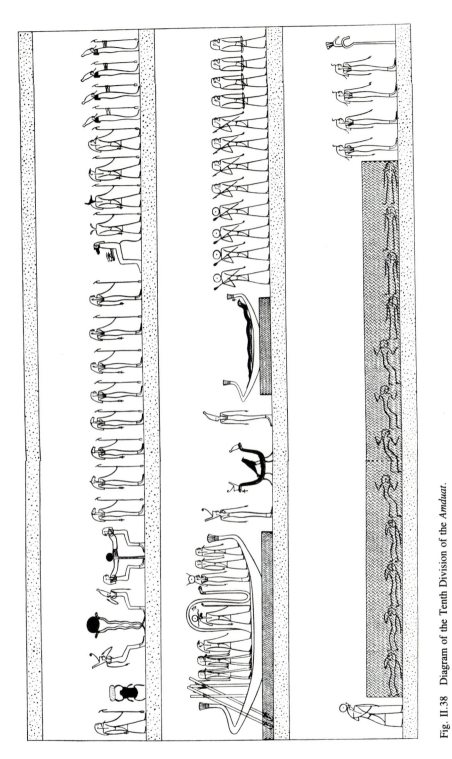

Fig. II.38  Diagram of the Tenth Division of the *Amduat*.

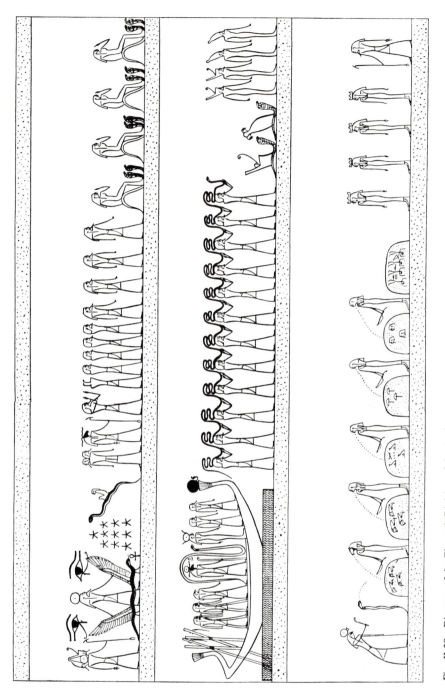

Fig. II.39  Diagram of the Eleventh Division of the *Amduat*.

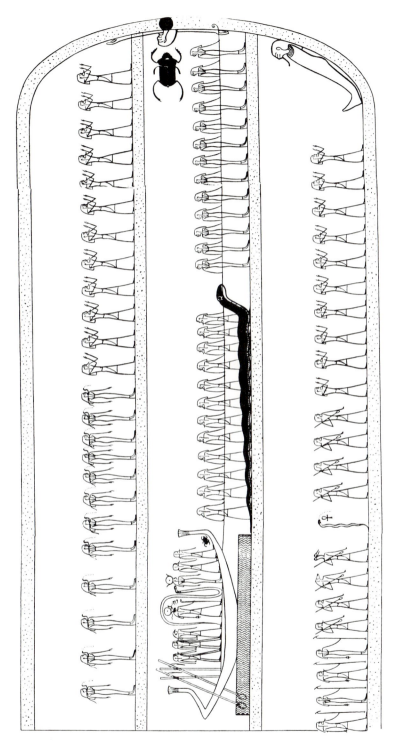

Fig. II.40  Diagram of the Twelfth Division of the *Amduat*.

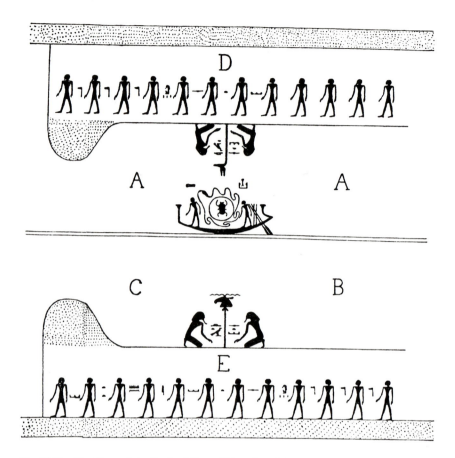

Fig. II.41   First Hour of the *Book of Gates*. Taken from Maystre and Piankoff, *Le Livre des portes,* Vol. 1, p. 2.

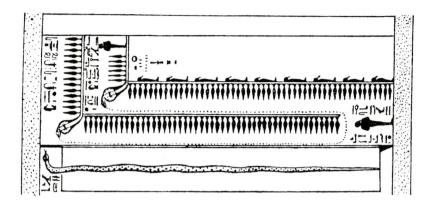

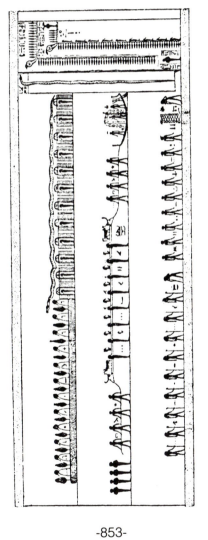

Fig. II.42  The gate at the end of the Third Hour of the *Book of the Gates* (called the "II<sup>e</sup> Division" by Maystre and Piankoff, Vol. 1, pp. 70, 75).

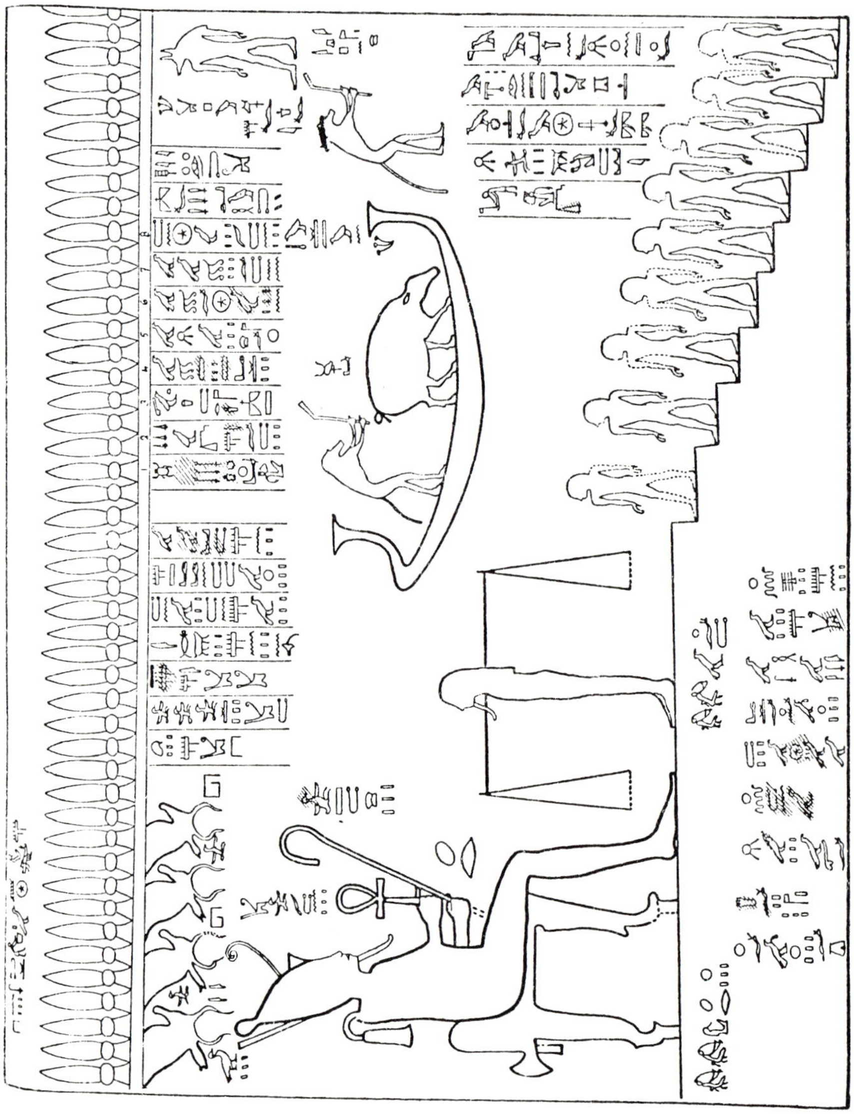

Fig. II.43   The Fifth Gate. From Maystre and Piankoff, Vol. 2, p. 87.

-854-

Fig. II.44 Eleventh Hour of the *Book of Gates*. Designated by Hornung as "Abbildung 62 75. und 76. Szene" in *Ägyptische Unterweltsbücher*, p. 288. Copied with the permission of Artemis Publishers in Zurich.

Fig. II.45 Another drawing from the Eleventh Hour (called by Piankoff: "X$^e$ Division"). Designated by Hornung as "Abbildung 64 80. Szene (Ausschnitt)." He uses the last term because he gives only 8 star-crowned goddesses. The figure here is taken from Maystre and Piankoff, Vol. 3, p. 88.

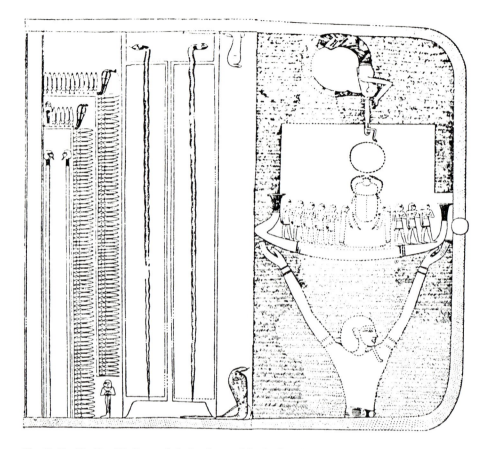

Fig. II.46   The Twelfth Gate and closing figure of the *Book of Gates*. Taken from Hornung, *Das Buch von den Pforten,* Teil II, p. 290, with the permission of Aegyptiaca Helvetica, Éditions de Belles Lettres, Geneva, Switzerland.

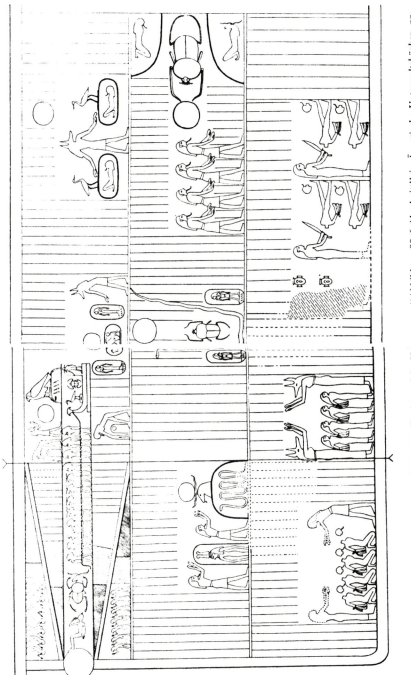

Fig. II.47 The Sixth Division of the *Book of Caverns*. Designated by Hornung as "Abbildung 80 6.Abschnitt" in *Ägyptische Unterweltsbücher*, pp. 404–05. Copied with the permission of Artemis Publishers Zurich.

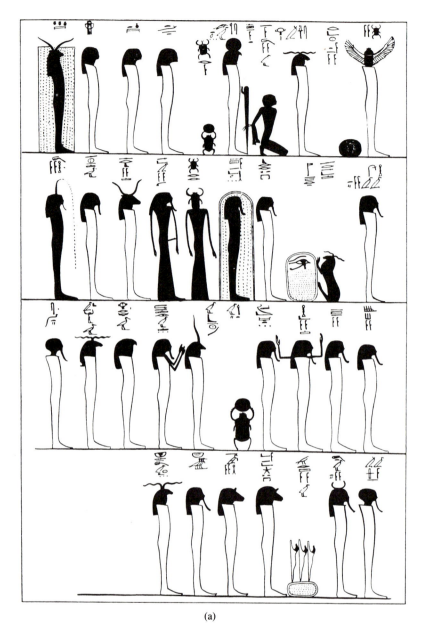

(a)

Fig. II.48  Figures (a) and (b) comprise the Forms of Re in the Tomb of Tuthmosis III.
According to Piankoff, *The Litany of Re,* pp. 14–15, and reproduced with the permission
of Princeton University Press.

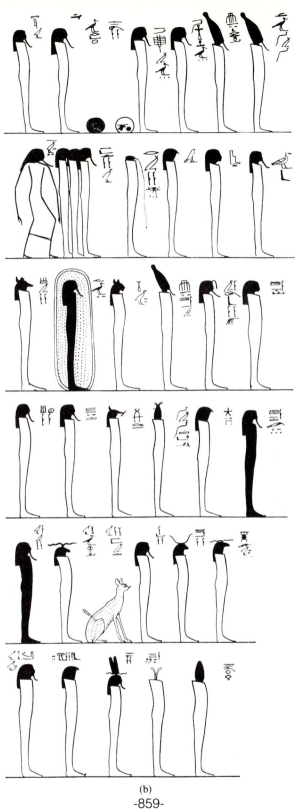

(a)

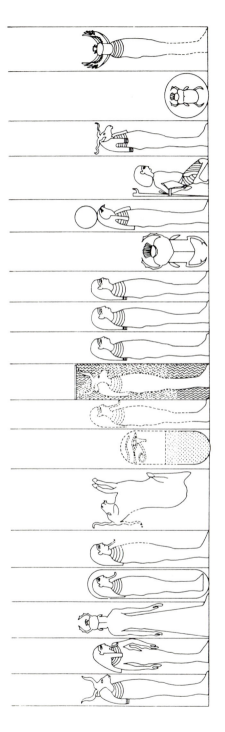
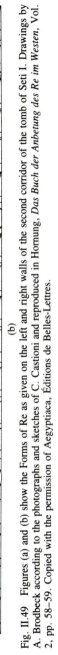
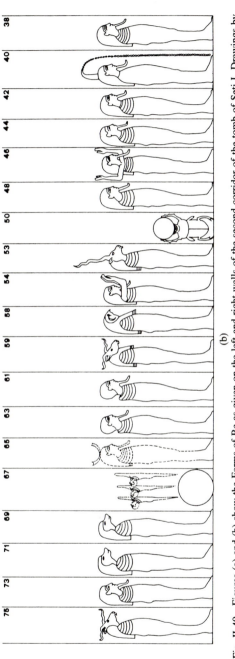

(b)

Fig. II.49 Figures (a) and (b) show the Forms of Re as given on the left and right walls of the second corridor of the tomb of Seti I. Drawings by A. Brodbeck according to the photographs and sketches of C. Castioni and reproduced in Hornung, *Das Buch der Anbetung des Re im Westen*, Vol. 2, pp. 58–59. Copied with the permission of Aegyptiaca, Éditions de Belles-Lettres.

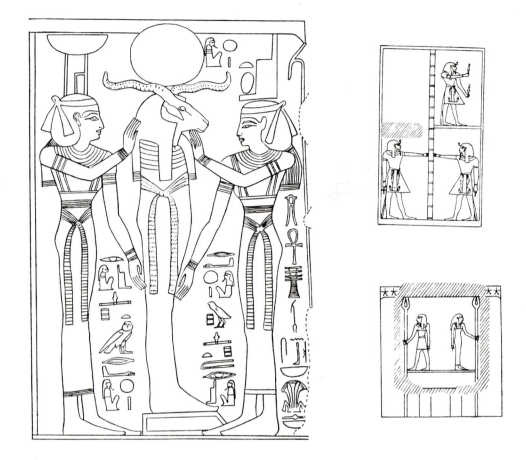

Fig. II.50   Representation of Re-Osiris, i.e. the United One, from the tomb of Queen Nefertari in the Valley of the Queens. Dynasty 19. Taken from Piankoff and Rambova, *The Tomb of Ramesses VI*, p. 34, with the permission of Princeton University Press.

Fig. II.51   The king helping to support the sky. From Hornung, *Der Ägyptische Mythos von der Himmelskuh*, p. 86. Courtesy of Éditions Universitaires, Fribourg, Switzerland.

Fig. II.52   Eternity *(nḥḥ)* and Everlastingness *(dt)* as personified gods supporting the sky. From Hornung, *ibid*. Courtesy of Éditions Universitaires, Fribourg, Switzerland.

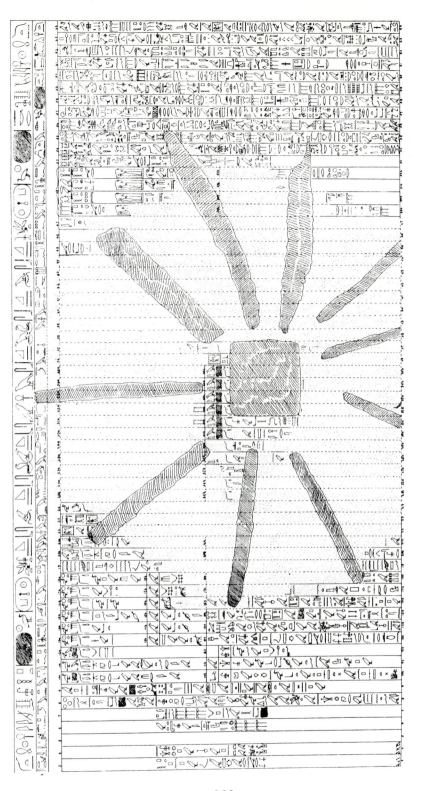

Fig. II.53  The Shabaka Stone. Dynasty 25. According to Breasted, "The Philosophy of a Memphite Priest," Tafel I. II.

-863-